Math
Makes Sense

5

Practice and Homework Book

Authors

Peggy Morrow   Maggie Martin Connell

PEARSON

Addison Wesley

Elementary Math Team Leader
Anne-Marie Scullion

Publisher
Claire Burnett

Publishing Team
Lesley Haynes
Enid Haley
Tricia Carmichael
Ellen Davidson
Ioana Gagea
Lynne Gulliver
Susan Lishman
Stephanie Cox
Judy Wilson
Nicole Argyropoulous

Design
Word & Image Design Studio Inc.

Typesetting
Computer Composition of Canada Inc.

ISBN 0-321-24224-6

Printed and bound in Canada.

14 15 16 DPC 13 12 11

PEARSON

Addison
Wesley

Contents

To the Teacher

This Practice and Homework Book provides reinforcement of the concepts and skills explored in the *Addison Wesley Math Makes Sense 5* program.

There are two sections in the book. The first section follows the sequence of *Math Makes Sense 5* Student Book. It is intended for use throughout the year as you teach the program. A two-page spread supports the content of each core lesson in the Student Book.

In each Lesson:

Quick Review summarizes the math concepts and terminology of the Student Book lesson.

The right page is the "homework" page, to be completed by the student with the assistance of a family member.

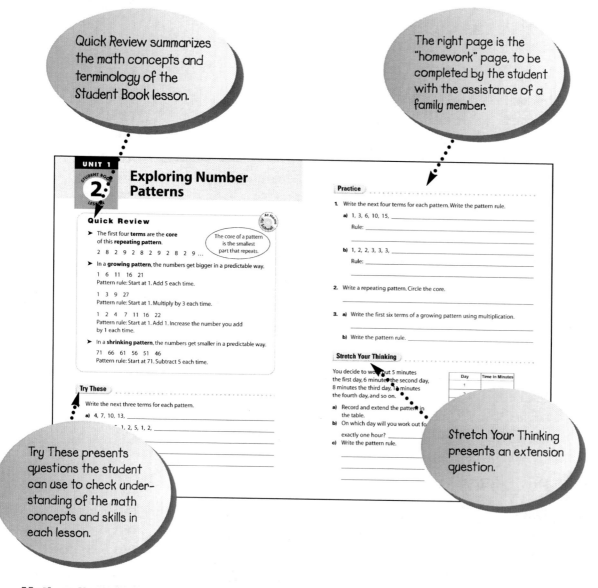

Try These presents questions the student can use to check understanding of the math concepts and skills in each lesson.

Stretch Your Thinking presents an extension question.

Math at Home

The second section of the book, on pages 167 to 178, consists of 3 pull-out **Math at Home** magazines. These fun pages contain intriguing activities, puzzles, rhymes, and games to encourage home involvement. The perforated design lets you remove, fold, and send home this eight-page magazine after the student has completed Units 3, 7, and 11.

To the Family

This book will help your child practise the math concepts and skills that have been explored in the classroom. As you assist your child to complete each page, you have an opportunity to become involved in your child's mathematical learning.

The left page of each lesson contains a summary of the main concepts and terminology of the lesson. Use this page with your child to review the work done in class. The right page contains practice.

Here are some ways you can help:
- With your child, read over the Quick Review. Encourage your child to talk about the content and explain it to you in his or her own words.
- Read the instructions with (or for) your child to ensure your child understands what to do.
- Encourage your child to explain his or her thinking.
- Some of the pages require specific materials. You may wish to gather items such as a centimetre ruler, index cards, a measuring tape, scissors, cubes numbered from 1 to 6, and paper clips.

Many of the Practice sections contain games that will also improve your child's math skills. You may have other ideas for activities your child can share with the rest of the class.

The **Math at Home** pull-out pages 167 to 178 provide more fun activities.

Number Patterns and Pattern Rules

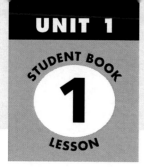

Quick Review

➤ Here is a number pattern:

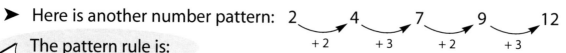

1 $\xrightarrow{+1}$ 2 $\xrightarrow{+3}$ 5 $\xrightarrow{+5}$ 10 $\xrightarrow{+7}$ 17

This pattern rule is:

Start at 1. Add 1. Increase the number you add by 2 each time.

➤ Here is another number pattern:

2 $\xrightarrow{+2}$ 4 $\xrightarrow{+3}$ 7 $\xrightarrow{+2}$ 9 $\xrightarrow{+3}$ 12

The pattern rule is:

Start at 2. Alternately add 2, then add 3.

➤ Here is another number pattern:

4 $\xrightarrow{+4}$ 8 $\xrightarrow{-1}$ 7 $\xrightarrow{+4}$ 11 $\xrightarrow{-1}$ 10

The pattern rule is:

Start at 4. Alternately add 4, then subtract 1.

Try These

1. Write the next 5 terms in each pattern.

   a) 25, 29, 30, 34, 35, _____, _____, _____, _____, _____

   b) 3, 4, 6, 9, 13, _____, _____, _____, _____, _____

   c) 16, 19, 17, 20, 18, _____, _____, _____, _____, _____

2. Write the first 4 terms of each pattern.
   a) Start at 6. Add 7 each time.

      _____, _____, _____, _____

   b) Start at 2. Alternately add 6, then subtract 2.

      _____, _____, _____, _____

Use a calculator when it helps.

1. Write the next 4 terms in each pattern. Write each pattern rule.

    a) 100, 125, 120, 145, 140, _____, _____, _____, _____

    Pattern rule: _____

    b) 85, 81, 90, 86, 95, _____, _____, _____, _____

    Pattern rule: _____

    c) 36, 72, 144, 288, 576, _____, _____, _____, _____

    Pattern rule: _____

2. Write the 6th term of each pattern.

    a) Start at 500. Alternately add 50, then subtract 15. _____

    b) Start at 85. Add 7. Increase the number you add by 3 each time. _____

    c) Start at 763. Subtract 13 each time. _____

    d) Start at 97. Alternately subtract 9, then add 2. _____

3. Start at 999. Write the first 7 terms of a pattern.

    Write the pattern rule.

    Pattern: _____

    Pattern rule: _____

Stretch Your Thinking

Write the first 5 terms of as many different patterns as you can that start with the terms 19, 24, …

_____

_____

_____

_____

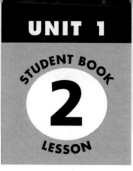

Creating Number Patterns

Quick Review

This is an **Input/Output machine**.
It can be used to make a growing pattern.

Input → ×9 → Output

Each input is multiplied by 9 to get the output.
If you input 1, the output is 9.
If you input 2, the output is 18.

Input	Output
1	9
2	18
3	27
4	36
5	45

The pattern rule is:

Start at 9. Add 9 each time.

Try These

1. Complete the table for each Input/Output machine.

   a)

   Input → +8 → Output

Input	Output
17	
16	
15	
14	
13	
12	
11	

   b)

   Input → ÷4 → Output

Input	Output
40	
36	
32	
28	
24	
20	
16	

2. Look at the tables in question 1. Write the pattern rule for each group of terms.

   a) the output numbers in part a) _____

   b) the input numbers in part b) _____

Practice

1. Complete the table for each Input/Output machine.

   a)

   Input →  → Output

Input	Output
93	
90	
87	
84	
81	

   b)

   Input →  → Output

Input	Output
305	
310	
315	
320	
325	

2. Look at the tables. Write the number and the operation in each machine.

   a)

   Input →  → Output

Input	Output
840	42
800	40
760	38
720	36
680	34

   b)

   Input →  → Output

Input	Output
11	143
20	260
29	377
38	494
47	611

 Stretch Your Thinking

1. The table shows the Input/Output from a machine.

   a) Write the number and operation for the machine. _____

   b) Write the pattern rule for the input numbers.

   _____

   c) Write the pattern rule for the output numbers. _____

Input	Output
3456	1152
3531	1177
3606	1202
3681	1227
3756	1252

Modelling Patterns

Quick Review

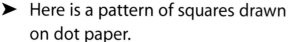
At Home
At School

➤ Here is a pattern of squares drawn on dot paper.

Square	Number of Dots on Perimeter
1	4
2	8
3	12
4	16
5	20

One pattern rule for the number of dots on the perimeter is:

Start at 4. Add 4 each time.

Another pattern rule for the number of dots is:

Multiply the square number by 4.

The number of dots on any perimeter is a multiple of 4.
The 10th square will have 10 × 4, or 40 dots on its perimeter.
57 is not a multiple of 4, so no square has 57 dots.
60 is a multiple of 4 because 15 × 4 = 60. So, the 15th square has 60 dots.

Try These

1. a) Complete the table for this pattern.

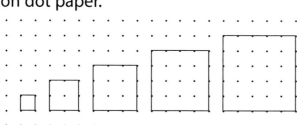

Triangle	Number of Dots on Perimeter
1	
2	
3	
4	

b) Which triangle will have 39 dots? _____ 57 dots? _____

c) Will any triangle have 46 dots? _____

Why or why not? _____

1. **a)** Complete the table for this pattern of regular hexagons.

Figure	Perimeter (units)
1	6
2	
3	
4	

   b) Write the pattern rule for the perimeters.

   _____

   c) Which figure will have a perimeter of 22 units? _____ 34 units? _____

   d) Predict the perimeter of the 10th figure. _____

   e) Will any figure have a perimeter of 55 units? Explain. _____

   _____

2. **a)** Complete the table for this pattern.

Figure	Perimeter (units)	Area (square units)
1		
2		
3		
4		

   b) Write the pattern rule for the areas.

   _____

   _____

1. **a)** Which figure in question 2 will have a perimeter of 120 units? _____

   What will its area be? _____

   b) Which figure in question 2 will have an area of 81 square units? _____

   What is its perimeter? _____

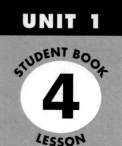
Using Patterns to Solve Problems

Quick Review

At Home
At School

One box holds 15 books.

➤ How many books will 2 boxes hold? 3 boxes? 4 boxes? Make a table.
Two boxes hold 30 books.
Three boxes hold 45 books.
Four boxes hold 60 books.

Number of Boxes	Number of Books
1	15
2	30
3	45
4	60

➤ Predict how many books 10 boxes will hold.

The pattern rule is:
Multiply the number of boxes by 15.

To predict the number of books 10 boxes will hold, multiply:
$10 \times 15 = 150$ Ten boxes will hold 150 books.

Try These

1. One concert ticket costs $11.
   a) Complete the table to find the cost of 7 tickets.

   b) Write a pattern rule for the cost.

   _____

   c) Predict the cost of 10 tickets. _____

   d) Extend the pattern. How many tickets can

   you buy with $155? _____

Number of Tickets	Cost ($)
1	
2	
3	
4	

1. Ivo practises the guitar 25 minutes every day.
   a) Make a table to show how many minutes Ivo practises in one week.
   b) How many minutes does Ivo practise in 10 days?

   _____

   c) How many minutes will Ivo practise in November?

   _____

   How many hours is that?

   _____

   d) How many days will it take Ivo to practise a total of 15 hours? _____

2. One minibus holds 18 students.
   a) Make a table to show how many students can ride in 6 minibuses.
   b) Write a pattern rule for the number of students.

   _____

   _____

   c) How many students can ride in 10 minibuses?

   _____

Stretch Your Thinking

1. Think about the minibuses in question 2 above.
   a) How many students can ride in 25 minibuses? _____
   b) How many minibuses are needed for 170 students? _____

Representing, Comparing, and Ordering Numbers

Quick Review

➤ Here are some ways to represent the number 135 294.

Standard Form	Words	Expanded Form
135 294	one hundred thirty-five thousand two hundred ninety-four	100 000 + 30 000 + 5000 + 200 + 90 + 4

➤ This place-value chart shows the population of 3 of Canada's provinces in 2001. You can use the chart to order the numbers from least to greatest.

Province	Hundred Thousands	Ten Thousands	One Thousands	Hundreds	Tens	Ones
Nova Scotia	9	0	8	0	0	7
Prince Edward Island	1	3	5	2	9	4
Saskatchewan	9	7	8	9	3	3

978 933 has the most hundred thousands and ten thousands. It is the greatest number.

135 294 has the least hundred thousands. It is the least number.

The order from least to greatest is: 135 294, 908 007, 978 933

Try These

1. Write each number in standard form.

   a) 200 000 + 80 000 + 4000 + 200 + 10 + 4 _284 214 or 284, 214_

   b) twenty-eight thousand one hundred sixty-two _28 162 or 28,162_

2. Order the numbers from greatest to least.

   a) 185 042   167 493   84 219 _185 042 - 167 493 - 84 219_

   b) 366 517   366 211   366 499 _366 517 - 366 499 - 366 211_

1. Use the data in the table.
   Arrange the countries in order from least to greatest coastline.

   Brazil, United States,
   Norway, Australia,
   Philipines,
   Indonesia, Canada

Country	Length of Coastline (kilometres)
Australia	25 760
Brazil	7 491
Canada	243 791
Indonesia	54 716
Norway	21 925
Philippines	36 289
United States	19 924

2. Find two 6-digit numbers in a newspaper or book.
   Write each number in standard and expanded form.

   a) _463,600 : 400,000 + 60,000 + 3,000 + 600_

   b) _354,050 : 300,000 + 50,000 + 4,000 + 50_

3. Write each number in words.

   a) 148 003 _one-hundred-forty-eight-thousand-three_

   b) 72 242 _seventy-two-thousand-two-hundred-forty-two_

4. Write the value of each underlined digit.

   a) 53<u>4</u> 649 _4,000_   b) 86 2<u>1</u>2 _10_

   c) 6<u>8</u>7 123 _80,000_   d) 15<u>8</u> 582 _8,000_

1. Use 6 of the digits from 1 to 9 to make each number. Use each digit only once.

   a) the greatest possible even number _987,654_

   b) the least possible odd number _123,457_

   c) the greatest possible number with 3 ten thousands _938,765_

UNIT 2

STUDENT BOOK 2 LESSON

Using Mental Math to Add

Quick Review

➤ Use mental math to add: 3584 + 4324
Use **compensation**.
3584 + 16 = 3600 ◄─── Add 16 to make 3600.
4324 – 16 = 4308 ◄─── Take away 16 to compensate.
3600 + 4308 = 7908

So, 3584 + 4324 = 7908

➤ Use mental math to add: 6327 + 348
Use the strategy of **adding on**.
Start with 6327.
Add on 3 hundreds, then 4 tens, then 8.

6327   6427   6527   6627   6637   6647   6657   6667   6675
    + 100   + 100   + 100   + 10   + 10   + 10   + 10   + 8

6327 + 348 = 6675

Try These

Use mental math to add.

1. Use compensation.

    a) 890 + 364 = _____   **b)** 2475 + 3540 = _____

    c) 7658 + 4143 = _____   **d)** 4891 + 1559 = _____

2. Use adding on.

    a) 5634 + 2252 = _____   **b)** 4167 + 232 = _____

    c) 1582 + 3217 = _____   **d)** 531 + 465 = _____

Play this game with a partner.

You will need:

10 counters each

Take turns.

➤ Choose 2 numbers from the Addends Box.

➤ Use mental math to find the sum.

➤ If the sum is on the game board, cover it with one of your counters.

➤ If the sum is not on the game board or is already covered, you lose a turn.

➤ The first player to get 4 in a row (horizontally, vertically, or diagonally) is the winner.

6842	5808	5695	4277
1435	4520	9463	3998
2742	2331	5857	3236
6619	4277	7141	5046

Addends Box

4326	5137
586	849
720	
1482	2516
3691	2004

Stretch Your Thinking

Use mental math to add: 3468 + 4153 + 2847 = _____

Describe the strategy you used.

_____

_____

_____

_____

Adding 3- and 4-Digit Numbers

At Home
At School

Quick Review

Ms. Blansky drove 2138 km in April and 3284 km in May.
How far did Ms. Blansky travel in the 2 months?

Add: 2138 + 3284

➤ Use expanded form to add.

2138 ⟶ 2000 + 100 + 30 + 8
+ 3284 ⟶ 3000 + 200 + 80 + 4
5000 + 300 + 110 + 12　= 5300 + 122 = 5422

➤ Use place value to add.

Add the ones:	Add the tens:	Add the hundreds:	Add the thousands:
12 ones	12 tens	4 hundreds	5 thousands
Regroup as 1 ten and 2 ones.	Regroup as 1 hundred and 2 tens.		
21**38** + 32**84** **2**	2**1**38 + 3**2**84 **22**	21**38** +32**84** **422**	**2**138 + **3**284 **5422**

Ms. Blansky travelled 5422 km.

Try These

1. a)　6825
　　　+ 3143
　　　　9,968

　　b)　3709
　　　+ 2867
　　　　6576

　　c)　5946
　　　+ 839
　　　　6,785

　　d)　8528
　　　+ 7637
　　　　16,165

　　e)　3579
　　　+ 6283
　　　　9,862

　　f)　2037
　　　+ 458
　　　　2495

　　g)　7382
　　　+ 1621
　　　　9,003

　　h)　4625
　　　+ 6673
　　　　11,298

Emilie Lesaffre

1. Use expanded form to add. Show your work.

   5673 ⟶

   + 8291 ⟶

2. Add.

   a) 3794   b) 3509   c) 7284   d) 8845
      + 6821   + 486   + 9613   + 7689
      10615   3,995   16,897   15534

   e) 4693   f) 7386   g) 1234   h) 4826
      + 3094   + 819   + 9876   + 319
      7787   8,205   11,110   5,145

3. Estimate first. Circle the letters next to the questions for which the sum will be greater than 8000.
   Then add to find all the sums.

   a) 2356   (b)) 6724   (c)) 4539   d) 3816
      + 4985   + 1934   + 3827   + 2647
      7,344   8,658   8,366   6,463

4. The Peace River is 1923 km long. The Mackenzie River is 2318 km longer than the Peace River. How long is the Mackenzie River?

   1923 + 2318 = 4241 the Mackenzie River long 2318 km,

5. Baldy Mountain is 832 m high. Mount Logan is 5127 m higher.
   How tall is Mount Logan?

   5127 + 832 = 5959 Mount Logan tall 5959

Two consecutive 4-digit numbers have a sum of 9173.

What are the 2 numbers? _____

Adding Three Numbers

At Home
At School

Quick Review

Add: 2472 + 3854 + 1962

➤ Add: 2472 + 3854   Then add 1962 to the result:

```
  1 1
  2472                          6326
+ 3854                        + 1962
  6326                          8288
```

➤ Use place value to add.

Add the ones:	Add the tens:	Add the hundreds:	Add the thousands:
8 ones	18 tens	22 hundreds	8 thousands
	Regroup as	Regroup as	
	1 hundred and	2 thousands and	
	8 tens.	2 hundreds.	

```
  2472        1           2 1         2 1
              2472        2472        2472
  3854        3854        3854        3854
+ 1962      + 1962      + 1962      + 1962
     8          88         288        8288
```

Estimate to check: 2000 + 4000 + 2000 = 8000

So: 8288 is a reasonable answer.

Try These

1. Add.

   a)   4723   b)   8962   c)   1357   d)   4572
        6415   3471   2468   3002
      + 3027   + 536   + 2389   + 5679

2. Estimate to check each answer in question 1. Show your work.

   a) _____   b) _____

   c) _____   d) _____

1. Find each sum.

   a) 1348
   2576
   + 3804

   b) 2893
   4627
   + 3284

   c) 3000
   2008
   + 6794

   d) 1941
   1939
   + 6821

2. Play this game with a partner.
   You will need a number cube labelled 1 to 6.

   ➤ Take turns to roll the number cube.
   On each roll, both players record the digit rolled in one of the boxes in the first addition grid.

   ➤ After 12 rolls, add.
   The player with the greater sum wins.

   ➤ Repeat with the other grids.

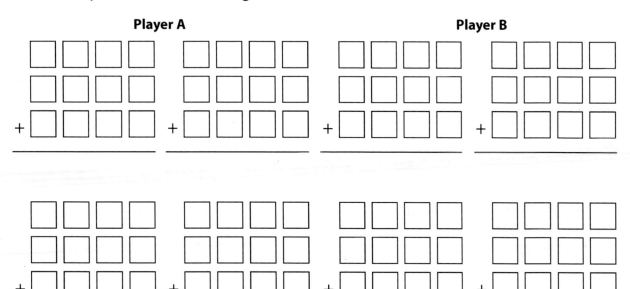

Stretch Your Thinking

The sum of three 4-digit numbers is 5638.

What might the numbers be? _____

UNIT 2

STUDENT BOOK 5 LESSON

Using Mental Math to Subtract

Quick Review

Use mental math to subtract: 4382 – 4194

➤ Make a friendly number.
   Add 6 to each number: 4388 – 4200
   4388 – 4200 = 188
   So, 4382 – 4194 = 188
➤ Think of 4194 in expanded form: 4000 + 100 + 90 + 4
   Subtract each number in turn.
   4382 – 4000 = 382
   382 – 100 = 282
   282 – 90 = 192
   192 – 4 = 188
   So, 4382 – 4194 = 188

Try These

Use mental math to subtract.

1. **a)** 5372 – 198 = _____

   b) 4682 – 2571 = _____

   c) 8588 – 4302 = _____

   d) 5227 – 419 = _____

   e) 6957 – 262 = _____

   f) 7641 – 3009 = _____

2. The first person walked on the moon in 1969.

   How long ago was that? _____

   _____

3. In 1984, Marc Garneau became the first Canadian in space. How long ago

   was that? _____

   _____

1. Use mental math to find each difference.
   Then use the letters next to the differences to solve this riddle.

> Why did the scientist
> have a wet head?

5421 – 3249 = _____ (W)

6729 – 4589 = _____ (N)

8315 – 2273 = _____ (V)

8726 – 6279 = _____ (A)

4000 – 2997 = _____ (H)

8297 – 4328 = _____ (B)

5315 – 2130 = _____ (O)

3600 – 1842 = _____ (S)

5725 – 3499 = _____ (I)

9098 – 7314 = _____ (R)

4797 – 2382 = _____ (T)

9285 – 190 = _____ (E)

1407 – 798 = _____ (G)

6394 – 3095 = _____ (M)

1003 9095   2172 2447 1758   1003 2447 6042 2226 2140 609

2447   3969 1784 2447 2226 2140 1758 2415 3185 1784 3299

Stretch Your Thinking

Use mental math to find two subtraction problems with the answer 1763.

_____

_____

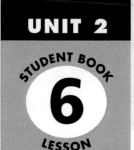
Subtracting with 4-Digit Numbers

Quick Review

Mount Everest is 8848 m high. Mount McKinley is 6194 m high.
How much higher is Mount Everest than Mount McKinley?
Subtract: 8848 – 6194

➤ Use place value to subtract.

Subtract the ones.	You cannot take 9 tens from 4 tens. Regroup 1 hundred as 10 tens.	Subtract the tens. Subtract the hundreds. Subtract the thousands.
8848 − 6194 ____ 4	$\overset{7\ 14}{88\cancel{4}8}$ − 6194 ____ 4	$\overset{7\ 14}{88\cancel{4}8}$ − 6194 ____ 2654

Mount Everest is 2654 m higher than Mount McKinley.

➤ Estimate to see if the answer is reasonable:
9000 – 6000 = 3000
3000 is close to 2654.
So, the answer is reasonable.

➤ Add to check if the answer is right.
2654 + 6194 = 8848
So, the answer is correct.

Try These

1. Subtract.

   a)   6847
        − 3928

   b)   9204
        − 3887

   c)   7684
        − 5375

   d)   5839
        − 4948

2. Estimate to see if each answer in question 1 is reasonable. Show your work.

   a) _____

   b) _____

   c) _____

   d) _____

1. Solve each problem. Show your work.
    a) Oleg has a 1939 penny in his coin collection.
       How old is the penny?

    _____

    b) Luisa's great grandmother was born in 1929.
       How old is she now?

    _____

2. Subtract.
    a) 5297   b) 8060   c) 4873   d) 7251
       – 3498   – 5309   – 2895   – 4168

    e) 9704   f) 3936   g) 2943   h) 3000
       – 5823   – 2847   – 1487   – 568

3. Subtract. Add to check your answers.
    a) 4826   Check: b) 9753   Check:
       – 2314   – 8658

Stretch Your Thinking

Find the missing digits.

```
  8 □ 6 □          □ 0 □ 4          6 □ 8 □
– □ 9 □ 7        – 6 □ 9 □        – □ 7 □ 2
─────────        ─────────        ─────────
  3 9 7 6            4 3 8          4 0 9 7
```

Multiplication and Division Facts to 144

Quick Review

Here are some strategies to help you multiply and divide.

➤ Use known facts to multiply.
To find 9×7:

$7 \times 7 = 49$

$2 \times 7 = 14$

$49 + 14 = 63$

So, $9 \times 7 = 63$

➤ Use related multiplication facts to find the quotient.
To find $96 \div 12$:

Think: 12 times which number is 96?

You know $12 \times \mathbf{8} = 96$.
So, $96 \div 12 = 8$.

 **Try These**

1. Multiply.

a) $11 \times 11 =$ _____   b) $11 \times 12 =$ _____   c) $6 \times 12 =$ _____

d) $12 \times 12 =$ _____   e) $11 \times 7 =$ _____   f) $7 \times 9 =$ _____

g) $7 \times 8 =$ _____   h) $9 \times 12 =$ _____   i) $8 \times 12 =$ _____

j) $10 \times 11 =$ _____   k) $9 \times 11 =$ _____   l) $12 \times 11 =$ _____

2. Divide.

a) $72 \div 8 =$ _____   b) $96 \div 12 =$ _____   c) $72 \div 9 =$ _____

d) $144 \div 12 =$ _____   e) $84 \div 7 =$ _____   f) $60 \div 12 =$ _____

g) $72 \div 6 =$ _____   h) $48 \div 12 =$ _____   i) $132 \div 11 =$ _____

j) $120 \div 12 =$ _____   k) $132 \div 12 =$ _____   l) $84 \div 12 =$ _____

Play this game with a partner.
You will need:
Counters of 2 colours
2 number cubes labelled 7 to 12

Take turns:
➤ Roll the number cubes and multiply the numbers that come up.
   Cover the product on the game board with one of your counters.
➤ The first player to cover 4 products in a vertical, horizontal, or diagonal
   line wins.

70	110	77	96	63
144	99	49	84	132
72	81	108	90	96
121	56	84	64	120
88	99	100	121	80

Stretch Your Thinking ·

Write as many division facts as you can that have a quotient of 8.

_____

_____

Multiplying with Multiples of 10

Quick Review

➤ Use place value to multiply by 10, 100, and 1000.
Find each product: 31×10 31×100 31×1000

31×1 ten $= 31$ tens $31 \times \textbf{10} = 31\textbf{0}$
31×1 hundred $= 31$ hundreds $31 \times \textbf{100} = 31\textbf{00}$
31×1 thousand $= 31$ thousands $31 \times \textbf{1000} = 31\,\textbf{000}$

➤ Use basic facts to multiply by multiples of 10, 100, and 1000.
Find each product: 6×400 6×4000

You know $6 \times 4 = 24$
6×4 hundreds $= 24$ hundreds 6×4 thousands $= 24$ thousands
So, $\textbf{6} \times \textbf{400} = \textbf{24}00$ $\textbf{6} \times \textbf{4000} = \textbf{24}\,000$

➤ Multiply 2 multiples of 10, 100, and 1000.
Find each product: 40×20 300×60

4 tens $\times 20 = 80$ tens   3 hundreds $\times 60 = 180$ hundreds
$\textbf{40} \times \textbf{20} = \textbf{80}0$ $\textbf{300} \times \textbf{60} = \textbf{18}\,000$

Try These

1. Multiply.

   a) $38 \times 10 =$ _____

   $38 \times 100 =$ _____

   $38 \times 1000 =$ _____

   b) $73 \times 10 =$ _____

   $73 \times 100 =$ _____

   $73 \times 1000 =$ _____

   c) $30 \times 10 =$ _____

   $30 \times 100 =$ _____

   $30 \times 1000 =$ _____

   d) $6 \times 9 =$ _____

   $6 \times 90 =$ _____

   $6 \times 900 =$ _____

   $6 \times 9000 =$ _____

   e) $12 \times 8 =$ _____

   $12 \times 80 =$ _____

   $12 \times 800 =$ _____

   $12 \times 8000 =$ _____

   f) $9 \times 7 =$ _____

   $9 \times 70 =$ _____

   $9 \times 700 =$ _____

   $9 \times 7000 =$ _____

2. Find each product.

   a) $40 \times 30 =$ _____

   b) $80 \times 50 =$ _____

   c) $20 \times 70 =$ _____

1. Multiply.

   a) $43 \times 10 =$ _____   **b)** $7 \times 90 =$ _____   **c)** $50 \times 70 =$ _____

   $43 \times 100 =$ _____ $7 \times 900 =$ _____ $50 \times 700 =$ _____

   $43 \times 1000 =$ _____ $7 \times 9000 =$ _____ $50 \times 7000 =$ _____

2. Find each product.

   a) $35 \times 100 =$ _____   **b)** $14 \times 900 =$ _____   **c)** $12 \times 70 =$ _____

   d) $17 \times 2000 =$ _____   **e)** $20 \times 80 =$ _____   **f)** $11 \times 8000 =$ _____

3. Find the total value of each set of bills.

   a) eighty $10 bills _____   **b)** sixty $20 bills _____

   c) seventy $50 bills _____   **d)** nine hundred $100 bills _____

4. A hamster eats 11 g of food a day. How much food does it eat in the month

   of April? _____

5. Margie packed 80 pamphlets in each of 70 envelopes. How many pamphlets

   did she pack? _____

6. Tickets to a concert cost $40 each. How much do 90 tickets cost?

   _____

7. A theatre has 60 rows of 30 seats. How many seats is that altogether?

   _____

Stretch Your Thinking

A payroll clerk writes 20 cheques for $600 and 12 cheques for $400. What is the
total amount of the cheques?

_____

_____

Using Mental Math to Multiply

Quick Review

➤ Multiply: 6×18

$6 \times 8 = 48$

$6 \times 10 = 60$

$48 + 60 = 108$

So, $6 \times 18 = 108$

➤ Multiply: 14×15

Half of 14 is 7.

Double 15 is 30.

$7 \times 30 = 210$

So, $14 \times 15 = 210$

➤ Multiply: 24×35

$24 = 12 \times 2$

$24 \times 35 = 12 \times 2 \times 35$

$= 12 \times 70$

$= 840$

So, $2 \times 35 = 840$

➤ Multiply: 203×6

$200 \times 6 = 1200$

$3 \times 6 = 18$

$1200 + 18 = 1218$

So, $203 \times 6 = 1218$

Try These

1. Multiply. Use mental math.

   a) $5 \times 45 =$ _____   **b)** $12 \times 45 =$ _____   **c)** $197 \times 3 =$ _____

   d) $18 \times 25 =$ _____   **e)** $2 \times 599 =$ _____   **f)** $14 \times 35 =$ _____

2. Use mental math. Find the product of 16×35 two different ways.
   Describe the strategies you used.

   _____   _____

   _____   _____

   _____   _____

3. Explain why $28 \times 25 = 7 \times 4 \times 25$.

   _____

Practice

1. Use mental math to find each product.

   a) 12 × 25 = _____ **b)** 58 × 26 = _____ **c)** 402 × 8 = _____

   d) 9 × 49 = _____ **e)** 36 × 18 = _____ **f)** 17 × 199 = _____

2. Use mental math to solve each problem.

   a) Emily has 8 books of stickers. Each book has 198 stickers. How many stickers does Emily have?

   _____

   b) A grocer ordered 26 boxes of oranges. Each box contains 3 dozen oranges. How many oranges did the grocer order?

   _____

   c) Suppose your heart beats 78 times a minute. How often does it beat in an hour?

   _____

3. Use mental math to complete this table.

×	25	16	42
23			
35			
14			
11			

Stretch Your Thinking

Which product is greater, 25 × 36 or 98 × 9? How much greater?

_____

_____

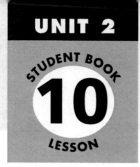
Multiplying 2-Digit Numbers

At Home
At School

Quick Review

Reba has 32 boxes of jumbo paper clips.
Each box contains 24 paper clips.
How many paper clips does Reba have?

Multiply: 32×24

Here is one way to multiply.
Break 24 apart.

$$\begin{array}{r} 32 \\ \times\,24 \\ \hline \end{array}$$

Multiply: 4×32 128
Multiply: 20×32 $+\,640$
Add.   768

$32 \times 24 = 768$

So, Reba has 768 paper clips.

Try These

1. Multiply.

a)
$$\begin{array}{r} 46 \\ \times\,32 \\ \hline +\;\;92 \\ 1380 \\ \hline 1472 \end{array}$$

b)
$$\begin{array}{r} 74 \\ \times\,23 \\ \hline 222 \\ +\,1480 \\ \hline 1702 \end{array}$$

c)
$$\begin{array}{r} 14 \\ \times\,18 \\ \hline 112 \\ +\,140 \\ \hline 252 \end{array}$$

d)
$$\begin{array}{r} 53 \\ \times\,22 \\ \hline 106 \\ +\,1060 \\ \hline 1166 \end{array}$$

2. Find each product.

a)
$$\begin{array}{r} 64 \\ \times\,23 \\ \hline 192 \\ 1280 \\ \hline 1472 \end{array}$$

b)
$$\begin{array}{r} 94 \\ \times\,12 \\ \hline 188 \\ +\,940 \\ \hline 1128 \end{array}$$

c)
$$\begin{array}{r} 82 \\ \times\,26 \\ \hline 492 \\ +\,1640 \\ \hline 2132 \end{array}$$

d)
$$\begin{array}{r} 34 \\ \times\,33 \\ \hline 102 \\ +\,1020 \\ \hline 1122 \end{array}$$

1. Play this game with a partner.
   You will need 10 cards labelled 0 to 9, placed in a paper bag.

   ➤ Each player draws a multiplication grid like this on paper.

   ➤ Take turns to draw a card from the bag.
     On each draw, both players record the digit in any box on their grids.
   ➤ Return the card to the bag after each draw.
   ➤ Continue until all the boxes are filled.
   ➤ Multiply using paper and pencil.
     Check each other's product.
   ➤ The player with the greater product wins a point.
   ➤ Play 5 rounds to determine an overall winner.

2. Solve each problem. Show your work.
   a) Bruce jogs a total of 25 km every week.
      How many kilometres does he jog in a year?

   b) Nya earns $17 a week baby-sitting.
      How much does she earn in 12 weeks?

Stretch Your Thinking

Find 2 consecutive 2-digit numbers whose product is 812.

Estimating Quotients

Quick Review

Here are some strategies you can use to estimate quotients.

➤ Estimate: 1984 ÷ 5
Look for **compatible numbers**.
1984 is close to 2000.
2000 is 20 hundreds.
20 hundreds ÷ 5 = 4 hundreds
            = 400
1984 ÷ 5 is about 400.

> Compatible numbers are pairs of numbers you can divide mentally.

➤ Estimate: 2236 ÷ 7
Use front-end estimation.
Find out how many digits the quotient will have.

7 × 100 = 700   ⟵ too low

7 × 1000 = 7000 ⟵ too high

The quotient will be in the hundreds.

Estimate the hundreds digit of the quotient.
There are 22 hundreds in 2236.
22 ÷ 7 is between 3 and 4, but closer to 3.
So, 2236 ÷ 7 is about 300.

Try These

1. Estimate each quotient.

a) 273 ÷ 5

b) 5942 ÷ 6

c) 4700 ÷ 8

_____

_____

_____

d) 984 ÷ 3

e) 1789 ÷ 9

f) 447 ÷ 4

_____

_____

_____

1. Estimate each quotient.

   a) 3517 ÷ 7   **b)** 2429 ÷ 5   **c)** 6324 ÷ 8   **d)** 4729 ÷ 6

   _____   _____   _____   _____

   e) 3209 ÷ 4   **f)** 2219 ÷ 3   **g)** 994 ÷ 5   **h)** 8848 ÷ 9

   _____   _____   _____   _____

2. Sydney has 893 collector's coins. He wants to mount them in groups of 9.

   About how many groups can he make? _____

3. Bruno travelled 2000 km in one week.

   About how far did he travel each day? _____

4. Maude made 1757 mL of strawberry fruit punch.

   About how much can she serve to each of 8 guests? _____

5. About how many Saturdays are there in 1 year? _____

6. One hundred ninety-one children signed up for basketball.

   About how many teams of 9 can the coaches make? _____

7. Crayons are packaged in boxes of 8.

   About how many boxes can be filled with 2507 crayons? _____

Stretch Your Thinking

Arnold estimated that 9385 ÷ 11 is about 800. Was his estimate high or low?
Explain.

_____

_____

_____

Dividing with Whole Numbers

Quick Review

Here are 2 ways to divide 5873 by 4.

➤ Use place value.

Divide the thousands.	Divide the hundreds.	Divide the tens.	Divide the ones.

Divide the thousands.
```
     1
4 ) 5 8 7 3
  - 4
    1
```

Divide the hundreds.
```
     1 4
4 ) 5 8 7 3
  - 4 ↓
    1 8
  - 1 6
      2
```

Divide the tens.
```
     1 4 6
4 ) 5 8 7 3
  - 4 ↓ ↓
    1 8
  - 1 6 ↓
      2 7
    - 2 4
        3 3
```

Divide the ones.
```
     1 4 6 8
4 ) 5 8 7 3
  - 4 ↓
    1 8
  - 1 6 ↓
      2 7
    - 2 4 ↓
        3 3
      - 3 2
          1
```

5873 ÷ 4 = 1468 R1

➤ Use short division.

$$4\overline{)5^18^27^33}$$
$$1\ 4\ 6\ 8\ \text{R1}$$

Try These

1. Divide.

a) 6⟌7632

b) 4⟌2536

c) 5⟌3561

d) 2⟌1283

(handwritten annotations: q: n:)

Fais sur une feuille

e) 3⟌5684

f) 7⟌1477

g) 8⟌5931

h) 9⟌6049

(handwritten annotations: q: R:)

1. Find each quotient. Use short division.

   a) 6)4632
   q: 772
   r: 0

   b) 8)5893
   q: 736
   r: 5

   c) 5)2482
   q: 496
   r: 2

   Fais

   d) 2)5363
   q: 2681
   r: 1

   e) 7)4907
   q: 707
   r: 0

   f) 4)6324
   q: 1773
   r: 2

   sur une

   g) 3)8621
   q: 2877
   r: 0

   h) 9)4136
   q: 459
   r: 5

   i) 7)3004
   q: 429
   r: 1

2. Divide. Use place value.

   feuille

   a) 3)5842
   q: 1947
   r: 1

   b) 6)7130
   q: 1188
   r: 2

   c) 8)6238
   q: 779
   r: 6

   fais sur feuille

3. In the cafeteria, students sit at tables for 8.

   How many tables are needed for 1563 students?

   Their are 195 tables and a 3 students

4. A ticket seller sold $2728 worth of movie tickets.

   How many tickets did she sell if each ticket cost $8?

Use the digits 4, 5, 6, 7, and 8 to make the greatest quotient with no remainder.

☐)☐☐☐☐

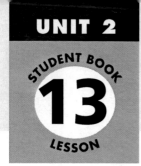
Solving Problems

Quick Review

➤ Maxine knits mittens and stocking caps and sells them at the market.
She charges $8 for a cap and $9 for a pair of mittens.
Last winter, Maxine's sales totalled $449.
She sold 25 pairs of mittens. How many caps did she sell?

First, find out how much she took in for mittens.
Multiply: $9 \times 25 = 225$

Maxine took in $225 for mittens.

Next, find out how much Maxine took in for the caps.
Subtract: $449 - 225 = 224$

Maxine took in $224 for caps.

Finally, find out how many caps Maxine sold.
Divide: $224 \div 8 = 28$

Maxine sold 28 stocking caps.

Try These

1. Munir worked on a farm for 3 weeks last summer.
The first week, he earned $150. The second week, he earned $24 more than
the first week. The third week, he earned $17 less than the second week.
How much money did Munir earn altogether?

   1st wk 150   2nd 150 + 24 = $174   3rd 174 - 17 $157

   150 + 174 + 157 = 681

2. Pan has 367 marbles. Seventy-eight marbles are green. One hundred
thirty-one are red. How many marbles of other colours does Pan have?

   131 + 78 = 209   367 - 209 = 158

Solve each problem. Show all your work.

1. Lonny uses 12 cups of flour to make 6 batches of cookies.
   How much flour will he need to make 18 batches of cookies?

   12 cups - 6 Batche = 6 cups
   1 Batch - 12 ÷ 6 = 2 cups   18 Batch - 18 × 2 = 36 cups

2. Liana packed 24 novels into each of 16 boxes.
   She packed 28 spelling books into each of 13 boxes.
   How many books did Liana pack?

   24 × 16 = 384   28 × 13 = 364   384 + 364 = 748

3. Kiara spent $273 on school clothes. She bought 2 pairs of jeans at $39 each,
   and 5 tops at $19 each. She spent the rest of the money on a pair of shoes.
   How much did Kiara spend on shoes?

   2 × 39 = $78   5 × 19 = 95$ 95 + 78 = 173
   273 - 173 = 100   shoes = $100

Stretch Your Thinking

Gene had 144 hens. He sold $\frac{1}{2}$ of them to Bonny and $\frac{1}{3}$ of them to Mark.
How many hens does Gene have left?

   144 ÷ 2 = 72   72 ÷ 3 = 24
   72 - 24 = 48

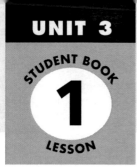

Naming and Sorting Polygons by Sides

Quick Review

A **polygon** is a closed figure with 3 or more straight sides.
Here are some ways to name polygons.

➤ Name polygons by the number of sides.

Triangle	Quadrilateral	Pentagon	Hexagon	Octagon
3 sides	4 sides	5 sides	6 sides	8 sides

➤ Name polygons by their vertices.
This is quadrilateral ABCD.
It has 4 sides: AB, AD, BC, and CD

➤ Name triangles by the number of equal sides.

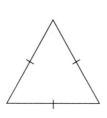  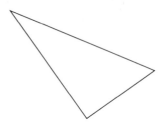

An **equilateral triangle** has all sides equal.   An **isosceles triangle** has 2 sides equal.   A **scalene triangle** has no sides equal.

Try These

1. Name each polygon.

a)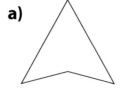

b)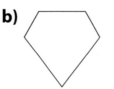

c)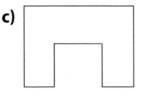

d)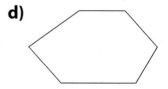

_____   _____   _____   _____

1. Draw each triangle.

    a) isosceles   **b)** scalene   **c)** equilateral

2. For each triangle, name the sides that are equal.

   a)   **b)**   **c)**   **d)**

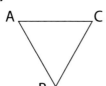 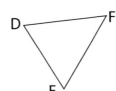  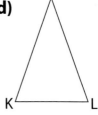

_____

3. Label each polygon with its name.

 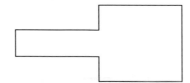 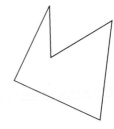

_____

 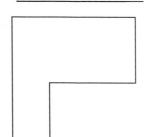 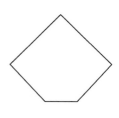

_____

Stretch Your Thinking

Why is it not possible to make an equilateral triangle on a geoboard?

_____

_____

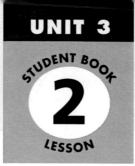
Measuring and Constructing Angles

At Home
At School

Quick Review

➤ We name angles according to their size.

Acute Angle

less than 90°

Right Angle

90°

Obtuse Angle

between 90° and 180°

➤ We use a ruler and a protractor to construct an angle with a given measure.
Here is how to construct a 60° angle.

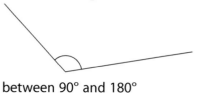

60°

Draw one arm of the angle.

Place the centre of the protractor at one end of the arm so that the base line of the protractor lies along the arm. Find 60° and make a mark.

Remove the protractor.
Draw the arm.
Label the angle.

Try These

1. Estimate the size of each angle, in degrees. Then measure.
   a)

   Estimate: _____

   Measure: _____

   b)

   Estimate: _____

   Measure: _____

1. Do this activity with a partner.
   Each of you secretly records an estimate of the size of the first angle.
   Work together to measure the angle.
   The person with the closer estimate gets a point.
   Repeat with the other angles.

   a)

   Measure: _____

   b)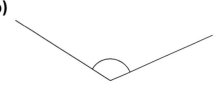

   Measure: _____

   c)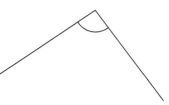

   Measure: _____

   d)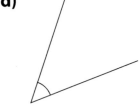

   Measure: _____

   e)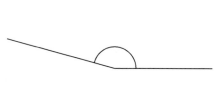

   Measure: _____

   f)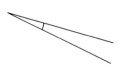

   Measure: _____

Stretch Your Thinking

Without using a protractor,
draw an angle that is close to 45°.
Explain how you did it.

_____

_____

_____

Naming and Sorting Polygons by Angles

Quick Review

➤ An **acute triangle** has all angles less than 90°.

A **right triangle** has one 90° angle.

An **obtuse triangle** has one angle greater than 90°.

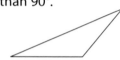

➤ A square has 4 right angles.

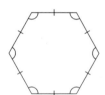

A rhombus has 2 pairs of equal angles.

A kite has 1 pair of equal angles.

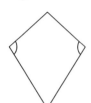

➤ A **regular polygon** has all sides equal and all angles equal.

An **irregular polygon** does not have all sides equal or all angles equal.

Try These

1. Name each triangle as acute, obtuse, or right.

   a)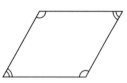

   b)

   c)

   _____   _____   _____

2. Is each polygon regular or irregular?

   a)

   b)

   _____   _____

1. Play this game with a partner.
   Player A:
   ➤ Secretly choose a polygon from below.

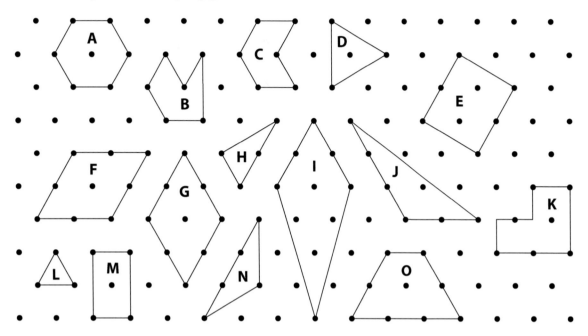

   Player B:
   ➤ Ask your partner "Yes/No" questions about the polygon.
   The questions can be about:
   • the type of angle (acute, right, or obtuse)
   • the number of a certain type of angle
   • equal or not equal angles
   • regular or irregular polygons

   ➤ Keep asking questions until you know the polygon.
   If you guess right, you get a point.

   Switch roles and keep playing until one player has 5 points.

Stretch Your Thinking

Explain why this figure is not a regular polygon.

_____

_____

Constructing Triangles

Quick Review

You can use a ruler and a protractor to construct a triangle.
Construct triangle ABC.
Make AB 3 cm long.
Make angle A 80°.
Make AC 2.5 cm long.

Draw side AB. Make it 3 cm long.	Measure an 80° angle at A.	Draw side AC. Make it 2.5 cm long.	Join C to B to make side BC.

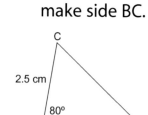

Try These

1. Use a ruler and protractor.
   Construct triangle EFG.
   Side EF is 7 cm long.
   Angle F is 90°.
   Side FG is 5.3 cm long.

2. What is the measure of:

   a) angle E? _____   **b)** angle G? _____

3. How long is side EG? _____

1. Construct each triangle using a ruler and a protractor.
   Label each triangle with the measures of all the sides and angles.

   a) Triangle JKL
   Side JL is 4 cm.
   Angle L is 60°.
   Side JK is 4 cm.

   b) Triangle XYZ
   Side XY is 5.8 cm.
   Angle X is 90°.
   Angle Y is 25°.

   c) Triangle TUV
   Side UV is 6.2 cm.
   Angle T is 70°.
   Angle U is 45°.

   d) Triangle PQR
   Angle P is 70°.
   Side PQ is 3.5 cm.
   Angle Q is 70°.

Stretch Your Thinking

Suppose you double the side lengths of a regular triangle.
What happens to the measure of the angles? Explain.

_____

_____

_____

Making Nets

Quick Review

A **net** shows all the faces of a solid, joined in one piece.
It can be folded to form the solid.
Here is one way to construct a net
for this triangular prism.

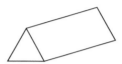

➤ Label each face of the solid.

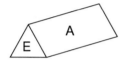

➤ Trace face A.

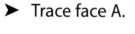

➤ Roll the solid over and trace face B.

➤ Roll the solid over and trace face C.

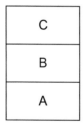

➤ Roll the solid over and trace face D.

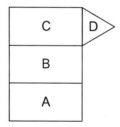

➤ Place the solid on the tracing of face A. Roll and trace face E.

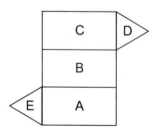

Try These

1. Name the solid each net would make.

   a)

   b)

   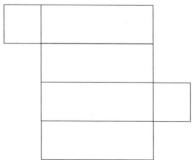

   c)

   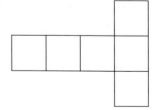

   _____   _____   _____

1. Circle the diagram that shows a net for the solid named.

   a) cube

   b) square pyramid

   c) triangular pyramid

2. Find a small box shaped like
   a rectangular prism.
   Carefully cut the box apart
   along its edges to form a net.
   Sketch your net.

3. What is the least number of faces

   you could use to make a net? _____

   What kind of solid would your net make?

   _____

Stretch Your Thinking

Sketch a net for a cube on the grid paper.
Write the letters T and B on 2 faces of
the net so that if the net was folded,
the T would be on the top and
the B on the bottom.

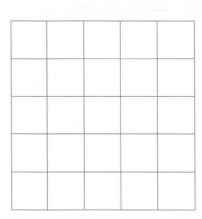

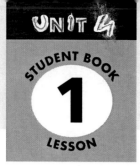
Tenths and Hundredths

At Home At School

Quick Review

➤ The ostrich egg is the biggest bird egg.
Here are some of its measurements.

Length: 17.8 cm
17.8 is a decimal.
It can also be written as a mixed
number: $17\frac{8}{10}$
Both are read as "seventeen and
eight-tenths."

Thickness of the shell: 0.15 cm
For a decimal less than 1, you write
a 0 in the ones place for 0 ones.
0.15 can be written as a fraction: $\frac{15}{100}$
Both are read as
"fifteen-hundredths."

Circumference: 39.87 cm
39.87 can be written as a mixed
number: $39\frac{87}{100}$
Both are read as "thirty-nine and
eighty-seven hundredths."

Mass: 1.06 kg
1.06 can be written as a mixed number:
$1\frac{6}{100}$
Both are read as "one and six-hundredths."

➤ You can use a place-value
chart to show decimals.

Ones		Tenths	Hundredths
0		1	5

Try These

1. Write a fraction or mixed number for each decimal.

   a) 2.7 $2\frac{7}{10}$ b) 9.36 $9\frac{36}{100}$ c) 8.04 $8\frac{4}{100}$ d) 0.56 $\frac{56}{100}$

2. Write a decimal for each fraction or mixed number.

   a) $6\frac{43}{100}$ 6.43   b) $7\frac{5}{10}$ 7.5   c) $\frac{9}{10}$ 0.9   d) $\frac{2}{100}$ 0.02

3. Write each number as a decimal.

   a) twelve and two-hundredths 12.02   b) three and nine-tenths 3.9

   c) seven and sixty-five hundredths 7.65   d) twenty and three-tenths 20.3

1. Draw Base Ten Blocks to model each decimal.

a)	b)	c)
2.6	0.47	1.05

2. Write each decimal as a mixed number or fraction.

   a) 8.47 _8 47_   b) 3.9 _3 + 3_   c) 0.62 _62_ ✓   d) 3.4 _3 4_ 3 + 4

   e) 7.6 _7 100 + 6_ ✓   f) 0.07 _7_ ✓   g) 12.38 _12 + 38_ ✓   h) 0.1 _1_ ✓ 10

   _76 10_   _100_   _100_   _10_

3. Write each mixed number or fraction as a decimal.

   a) $25\frac{6}{10}$ _25,6_ ✓   b) $9\frac{8}{100}$ _9,08_ ✓   c) $7\frac{3}{10}$ _7,3_ ✓   d) $\frac{49}{100}$ _0,49_ ✓

   e) $\frac{1}{100}$ _0,01_ ✓   f) $14\frac{4}{10}$ _14,4_ ✓   g) $\frac{8}{10}$ _0,8_ ✓   h) $4\frac{17}{100}$ _4,17_ ✓

4. Write a decimal with:

   a) a 7 in the tenths place _0,7_   b) a 9 in the hundredths place _0,09_

   c) a 6 on the ones place _6_   d) a 0 in the tenths place _0,0_

Use the numbers 1, 5, and 9 to make as many different decimals as you can.

_1,59 ✓ 1,95 ✓ 9,51 ✓ 9,15 ✓ 5,91 ✓ 5,19 ✓_

_15,9 ✓ 59,1 ✓ 95,1 ✓ 91,5 ✓ 19,5 ✓ 51,9 ✓ 59,1 ✓ 95,1 ✓_

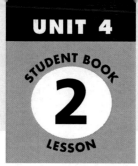

Equivalent Decimals

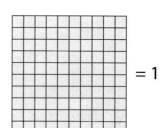

Quick Review

One row of this hundredths grid is
one tenth of the grid.
Each small square is one hundredth
of the grid.

= 1

7 rows are 7 tenths.
0.7

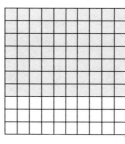

70 squares
are 70 hundredths.
0.70

Both 0.7 and 0.70 name the shaded part of the grid.
So, 0.7 = 0.70
Decimals that name the same amount are called **equivalent decimals.**

Try These

1. Write two equivalent decimals that name each shaded part.
   a) 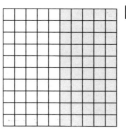 b) c) d)

   a) 0.50 0.5   b) 0.3 0.30   c) 0.7 $\frac{7}{100}$ d) 0.1 0.10

2. Write an equivalent decimal for each number.

   a) 1.6 _1 + 60_   b) 0.70 _0.7_   c) 3.90 _3.9_   d) 5.5 _5.5_

   e) 0.80 _0.8_   f) 0.1 _0.1_   g) 0.30 _0.3_   h) 4.60 _4.6_

   i) 2.40 _2.4_   j) 8.2 _8.2_   k) 0.50 _0.5_   l) 1.10 _1.1_

1. Colour the grids to show each decimal.
   Write an equivalent decimal.

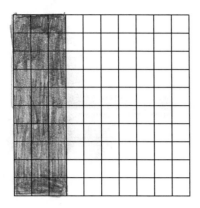 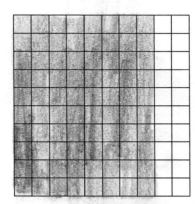 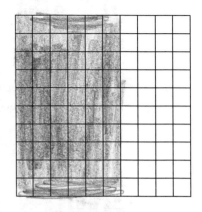

a) 0.3 ___3___
$\overline{10}$

b) 0.80 ___80___
$\overline{100}$

c) 0.6 ___6___
$\overline{10}$

2. Play this game with a partner.
   You will need:
   15 pairs of cards with 2 equivalent decimals (for example, 0.4 and 0.40,
   1.5 and 1.50).
   ➤ Shuffle the cards and turn them face down on a table in 6 rows of 5.
   ➤ Take turns to turn over 2 cards.
   If the cards name equivalent decimals, keep the cards and play again.
   If the cards do not name equivalent decimals, turn them face down again.
   ➤ Play until there are no cards left on the table.
   ➤ The player with the most cards wins.

Stretch Your Thinking

Gabriel is making a design on a hundredths grid. He says he will colour 0.6 of the
grid red, and 0.6 black. Will Gabriel's plan work? Explain.

_____

_____

_____

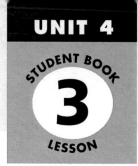
Comparing and Ordering Decimals

Quick Review

At Home
At School

Here are the heights of 3 children.

Here are 2 ways to put the children in order from shortest to tallest.

Name	Height (m)
Ruben	1.5
Jamil	1.54
Sandy	1.4

➤ Write each decimal in a place-value chart.

Ones	Tenths	Hundredths
1	5 ←	0
1	5	4
1	4 ←	0

Use equivalent decimals.

5 tenths is 50 hundredths.

4 tenths is 40 hundredths.

Look at the whole number parts. All 3 numbers have 1 one.

Look at the decimal parts. 40 hundredths is the least. 54 hundredths is the greatest.

So, the heights from shortest to tallest are 1.4 m, 1.5 m, 1.54 m.

➤ Use a number line. Mark a dot for each number.

```
        1.4              1.5   1.54
  +--+--+--+--+--+--+--+--+--+--+--+--+--+--+--+
1.30          1.40          1.50          1.60
```

Read the numbers from left to right: 1.4, 1.5, 1.54

So, the order of the children from shortest to tallest is: Sandy, Ruben, Jamil.

Try These

1. Use >, <, or = to make each statement true.

   a) 0.25 __<__ 0.41

   b) 6.2 __=__ 6.20

   c) 2.04 __>__ 2.01

   d) 1.37 __<__ 1.4

   e) 2.18 __>__ 2.06

   f) 8.50 __=__ 8.5

2. Write the decimals in order from least to greatest.

   a) 3.56, 3.74, 3.42 __3.42, 3.56, 3.74__ 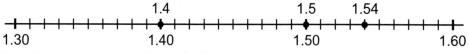 b) 1.41, 0.99, 1.3 __0.99, 1.3, 1.41__

Practice

1. Write the decimals in order from greatest to least.

   a) 6.3, 4.8, 6.13 _6.3, 6.13, 4.8_   b) 0.84, 0.26, 0.9 _0.9, 0.84, 0.26_

   c) 3.7, 3.74, 3.9 _3.9, 3.74, 3.7_   d) 1.61, 0.94, 0.4 _1.61, 0.94, 0.4_

2. Write a decimal to make each statement true.

   a) 4.05 > _4.02_   b) 0.21 < _0.24_   c) 6.3 = _6.30_

   d) 5.1 < _5.2_   e) 7.63 > _7.60_   f) 9.99 > _9.97_

3. Use the number lines to order each set of numbers from greatest to least.
   a) 0.4, 0.36, 0.44

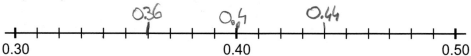

   b) 1.75, 1.83, 1.7

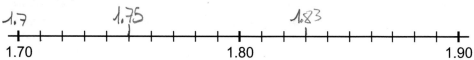

   c) 2.13, 2.04, 2.1

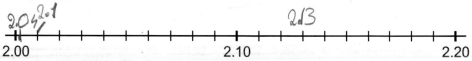

4. Write 3 decimals to match each description.

   a) greater than 0.94 _0.97_

   b) less than 1.1 _0.9_

   c) greater than 2.7 and less than 3.12 _2.71   3.11_

Stretch Your Thinking

1. Use the digits 3, 5, and 7.

   a) Write a decimal between 5 and 6. _5.3_

   b) Write a decimal greater than your answer to part a. _7.5_

   c) Write a decimal less than your answer to part a. _3.5_

Rounding Decimals

Quick Review

Here are the lengths of 3 spiders. To write an estimate of these lengths, you can **round** to the nearest centimetre.

Spider	Length (cm)
Turret	1.71
Wolf Spider	2.11
Golden Silk	2.50

You can use a number line to round decimals.

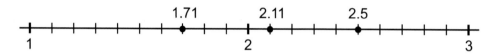

1.71 is between
1 and 2, but closer to 2.
So, 1.71 cm rounds up
to 2 cm.

2.11 is between
2 and 3, but closer to 2.
So, 2.11 cm rounds
down to 2 cm.

2.50 is halfway
between 2 and 3.
So, 2.50 cm rounds
up to 3 cm.

Try These

1. Use the number line to round each decimal to the nearest whole number.

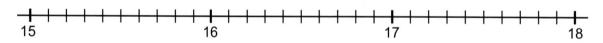

a) 16.3 _____   b) 15.5 _____   c) 15.2 _____   d) 17.1 _____

e) 17.7 _____   f) 16.9 _____   g) 17.4 _____   h) 16.5 _____

2. Round to the nearest whole number.

a) 37.3 _____   b) 84.8 _____   c) 27.1 _____   d) 12.5 _____

e) 8.6 _____   f) 13.2 _____   g) 19.4 _____   h) 31.8 _____

3. Circle the decimals that could be rounded to each boxed number.

a) ⬜5 4.5, 5.6, 4.7, 5.3   b) ⬜1 0.4, 0.9, 1.4, 1.7

1. Round to the nearest whole number.

   a) 44.63 _____ **b)** 87.12 _____ **c)** 33.2 _____ **d)** 55.50 _____

   e) 0.81 _____ **f)** 1.02 _____ **g)** 3.51 _____ **h)** 6.49 _____

2. Round to the nearest dollar.

   a) $0.87 _____ **b)** $1.50 _____ **c)** $4.29 _____ **d)** $13.69 _____

   e) $12.95 _____ **f)** $2.13 _____ **g)** $5.25 _____ **h)** $17.03 _____

3. Circle the decimals that could be rounded to each middle number.

   a) 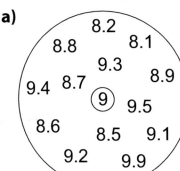 **b)** 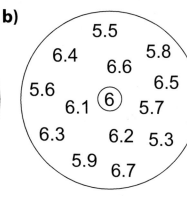 **c)**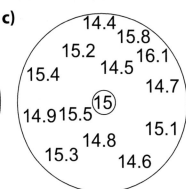

4. Arnold measured the length of the hall to the nearest hundredth of a metre. The length of the hall was 13 m when rounded to the nearest metre. What are the longest and shortest possible lengths of the hall?

   _____

Use the digits 2, 5, and 9.
Write as many decimals as you can.
Round each decimal to the nearest whole number.

_____

_____

Estimating Sums and Differences

Quick Review

➤ The penny has a mass of 2.35 g. The nickel has a mass of 3.95 g.
To estimate the combined mass of these coins:
Estimate: 2.35 + 3.95

Round each decimal to the nearest whole number.
2.35 rounds to 2.
3.95 rounds to 4.
Add the rounded numbers: 2 + 4 = 6
The combined mass of a penny and
a nickel is about 6 g.

*You get another estimate
if you round just 1 number.*
2.35 + 4 = 6.35
So, 2.35 + 3.95 is about 6.35.

➤ The quarter has a width of 23.88 mm. The penny has a width of 19.05 mm.
To estimate the difference in these widths:
Estimate: 23.88 − 19.05

Round one or both decimals to a "nice number."
Round 23.88 down to 23.85.
23.85 − 19.05 = 4.80
The difference in widths of a quarter
and a penny is about 4.80 mm.

*You get another estimate if
you round up to a "nice number."*
Round 23.88 to 23.90.
23.90 − 19.05 = 4.85
So, 23.88 − 19.05 is about 4.85.

Try These

1. Estimate each sum or difference.

a) 4.7 + 8.9 _____

b) 5.1 + 6.3 _____

c) 7.8 + 4.2 _____

d) 6.4 + 3.8 _____

e) 3.2 − 0.9 _____

f) 6.8 − 4.9 _____

g) 11.7 − 3.1 _____

h) 8.1 − 2.2 _____

i) 9.51 + 6.84 _____

j) 5.50 + 4.89 _____

k) 9.76 − 5.84 _____

l) 8.06 − 7.78 _____

Practice

1. Estimate each sum or difference.

   a) 9.7 + 8.2 _____ **b)** 12.1 – 4.9 _____ **c)** 18.5 – 11.8 _____

   d) 6.25 + 7.6 _____ **e)** 14.89 – 7.2 _____ **f)** 7.31 + 8.67 _____

   g) 12.36 – 4.15 _____ **h)** $15.78 – $1.98 _____ **i)** 25.3 + 12.9 _____

   j) 14.8 – 0.9 _____ **k)** $18.49 – $1.25 _____ **l)** 11.38 – 9.12 _____

2. Use the data in the sign.

   a) Sandar has $5. Which 2 fruits can he buy?

   _____

   _____

   b) Lucy has $8. Which 3 fruits can she buy?

Fruit Stand
Watermelon $5.95
Cantaloupe $4.19
Mango $1.99
Prickly Pear $2.19
Grapes $3.15

   _____

   _____

   c) Owen has 2 toonies. Does he have enough money to buy a mango and

   a prickly pear? Explain. _____

   _____

   d) Trudy bought 2 mangos and grapes. About how much change did

   Trudy get from $10? _____

   _____

3. Azem estimated that 9.65 – 6.25 is about 3.50. How did he estimate the

   difference? _____

   _____

Stretch Your Thinking

A bird sanctuary is 124.85 m long and 115.37 m wide.
Celeste walked around the perimeter of the bird sanctuary.

About how far did she walk? _____

_____

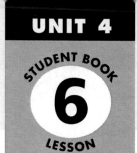

STUDENT BOOK
6
LESSON

Adding Decimals

At Home
At School

Quick Review

Madison rode her bike 11.76 km on Saturday and 6.18 km on Sunday.
What total distance did Madison ride?

You can use place value to add 11.76 + 6.18.
First estimate.
11.76 rounds to 12.
6.18 rounds to 6.
12 + 6 = 18

Step 1: Record the numbers.
Align them as they are
aligned in the
place-value chart.

Tens	Ones	•	Tenths	Hundredths
1	1	•	7	6
	6	•	1	8

$$
\begin{array}{r}
11.76 \\
+\ 6.18 \\
\end{array}
$$

Step 2: Add as you would with
whole numbers.

$$
\begin{array}{r}
\overset{1}{1}1.76 \\
+\ 6.18 \\
\hline
17.94 \\
\end{array}
$$

*Add the hundredths.
Regroup 14 hundredths
as 1 tenth 4 ones.
Add the tenths.
Add the ones.
Add the tens.*

17.94 is close to the estimate of 18, so the answer is reasonable.

Try These

1. Estimate first. Then add.

a) $\begin{array}{r} 3.4 \\ +\ 9.3 \\ \end{array}$

b) $\begin{array}{r} 6.8 \\ +\ 4.7 \\ \end{array}$

c) $\begin{array}{r} 7.54 \\ +\ 3.62 \\ \end{array}$

d) $\begin{array}{r} \$8.09 \\ +\ \$7.68 \\ \end{array}$

e) $\begin{array}{r} 25.2 \\ +\ 13.9 \\ \end{array}$

f) $\begin{array}{r} \$43.16 \\ +\ \$\ 8.97 \\ \end{array}$

g) $\begin{array}{r} 0.97 \\ +\ 1.23 \\ \end{array}$

h) $\begin{array}{r} 18.40 \\ +\ 26.60 \\ \end{array}$

1. Add.

a) 9.7
  + 4.9

b) 16.3
  + 12.8

c) $4.07
  + $8.63

d) 21.60
  + 14.73

e) 35.7
  + 98.6

f) $1.54
  + $3.65

g) 6.28
  + 12.32

h) 47.37
  + 19.08

2. Play this game with a partner.
You will need paper, pencils, and a number cube, labelled 1 to 6.
The object of the game is to get the greater sum.

➤ Draw an addition grid like this on your paper:

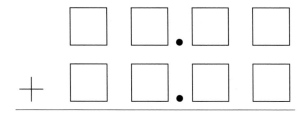

➤ Take turns to roll the number cube. Record the number rolled in any box
in your addition grid.
➤ Continue until all the boxes in your grid are full.
➤ Add. The player with the greater sum scores 1 point.
➤ Play 4 more rounds to find the overall winner.
➤ Play the game again. This time, try to get the lesser sum.

Stretch Your Thinking

Find 2 decimals with a sum of 9.76.
Do this in as many ways as you can.

_____

_____

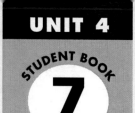
Subtracting Decimals

Quick Review

Joline grew 2 pumpkins in her garden.
The masses of her pumpkins are 7.05 kg and 9.84 kg.
What is the difference in the masses?

You can use place value to find 9.84 – 7.05.
First estimate.
9.84 rounds to 10.
7.05 rounds to 7.
10 – 7 = 3

Step 1: Record the numbers.
Align them as they are aligned
in the place-value chart.

Ones	●	Tenths	Hundredths
9	●	8	4
7	●	0	5

$$9.84$$
$$- 7.05$$

Step 2: Subtract as you would with whole numbers.

$$\overset{7\ 14}{9.8\cancel{4}}$$
$$- 7.05$$
$$2.79$$

Regroup 1 tenth as 10 hundredths.
Subtract the hundredths.
Subtract the tenths.
Subtract the ones.

2.79 is close to the estimate of 3, so the answer is reasonable.

Try These

1. Estimate first. Then subtract.

a) 6.8
   – 4.3

b) 8.5
   – 0.9

c) 2.67
   – 1.38

d) $12.45
   – $ 8.68

1. Subtract.

a)　　9.4
　　− 6.8

b)　　25.8
　　− 16.9

c)　　7.04
　　− 2.13

d)　　8.62
　　− 5.74

e)　14.25
　− 8.37

f) $20.15
　− $ 9.48

g)　84.08
　− 47.16

h)　52.34
　− 26.89

2.

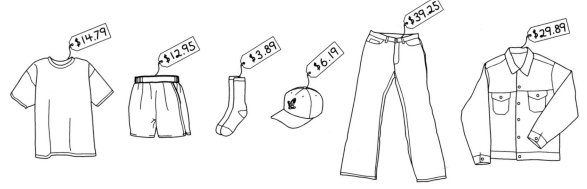

a) How much more than the jacket do the jeans cost? _____

b) Jerry paid for a baseball hat with a $10 bill.

   How much change did he get? _____

c) Sylvie bought a shirt and a pair of socks. She gave the clerk $20.

   How much change did she get? _____

d) What is the difference in price between the least expensive and most

   expensive items? _____

e) Which 2 items have each difference in price?

   $26.30 _____

   $15.10 _____

   $6.76 _____

Name 2 decimals whose difference is between 9 and 10, but closer to 9.

_____

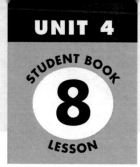
Multiplying Decimals by 10 and 100

At Home
At School

Quick Review

You can use mental math to multiply a decimal by 10 and 100.

➤ When you multiply a decimal by 10, the digits shift 1 place to the left. You can show this by moving the decimal point 1 place to the right.

$3.58 \times 10 = 35.8$

$5.9 \times 10 = 59$ ⟵ *You do not have to put a decimal point after a whole number.*

$26.73 \times 10 = 267.3$

➤ When you multiply a decimal by 100, the digits shift 2 places to the left. You can show this by moving the decimal point 2 places to the right.

$6.34 \times 100 = 634$

$9.7 \times 100 = 970$ ⟵ *You write a zero when there are no digits in the ones place.*

$23.62 \times 100 = 2362$

Try These

1. Multiply. Use mental math.

   a) $5.2 \times 10 = \underline{52}$

   b) $7.8 \times 10 = \underline{78}$

   c) $6.4 \times 10 = \underline{64}$

   d) $3.45 \times 10 = \underline{34.5}$

   e) $0.79 \times 10 = \underline{7.9}$

   f) $18.08 \times 10 = \underline{180.8}$

2. Use mental math to multiply.

   a) $6.45 \times 100 = \underline{645}$

   b) $7.38 \times 100 = \underline{738}$

   c) $2.68 \times 100 = \underline{268}$

   d) $8.5 \times 100 = \underline{850}$

   e) $7.3 \times 100 = \underline{730}$

   f) $1.8 \times 100 = \underline{180}$

   g) $32.41 \times 100 = \underline{3241}$

   h) $52.04 \times 100 = \underline{5204}$

   i) $0.93 \times 100 = \underline{93}$

3. Use the place-value chart. Record each product in the chart.

   a) 3.89×100
   b) 2.51×10
   c) 0.62×10

Hundreds	Tens	Ones •	Tenths	Hundredths
		•		
		•		
		•		

1. Use mental math to multiply.

   a) 9.2 × 10 = _____   **b)** 3.76 × 10 = _____   **c)** 0.4 × 10 = _____

       9.2 × 100 = _____   3.76 × 100 = _____   0.4 × 100 = _____

   d) 2.06 × 10 = _____   **e)** 0.59 × 10 = _____   **f)** 74.24 × 10 = _____

       2.06 × 100 = _____   0.59 × 100 = _____   74.24 × 100 = _____

2. Multiply. Use mental math.

   a) 4.8 × 10 = _____   **b)** 7.6 × 100 = _____   **c)** 4.25 × 100 = _____

   d) 0.09 × 100 = _____   **e)** 56.78 × 10 = _____   **f)** 32.40 × 100 = _____

3. Use mental math to solve each problem.
   a) A penny has a thickness of 1.45 mm.

   How high would a pile of 100 pennies be? _____

   b) One jar of peanut butter costs $3.95. How much would 10 jars cost?

   _____

   c) Omar walks 2.78 km each day. How far does Omar walk in 10 days?

   _____

   d) Tiara needs 14.25 m of string for each kite that she makes.
   How much string would Tiara need for 100 kites?

   _____

Stretch Your Thinking

A honeybee travels about 182.9 km to collect enough nectar to produce 1 g of honey. How far must it travel to collect enough nectar to produce 10 g of honey? 100 g of honey? 1 kg of honey?

_____

_____

Dividing Decimals by 10

Quick Review

You can use mental math to divide a decimal by 10.

➤ When you divide a decimal by 10, the digits shift 1 place to the right. You can show this by moving the decimal point 1 place to the left.

$32.6 \div 10 = 3.26$ $278.4 \div 10 = 27.84$

$7.6 \div 10 = 0.76$ $0.2 \div 10 = 0.02$

When there are no ones, you use zero as a placeholder.

Sometimes you need zero as a placeholder in the tenths place.

Try These

1. Use mental math to divide.

   a) $17.5 \div 10 =$ _____   **b)** $26.4 \div 10 =$ _____   **c)** $89.3 \div 10 =$ _____

   d) $613.2 \div 10 =$ _____   **e)** $740.8 \div 10 =$ _____   **f)** $309.1 \div 10 =$ _____

   g) $3.5 \div 10 =$ _____   **h)** $9.4 \div 10 =$ _____   **i)** $6.1 \div 10 =$ _____

   j) $0.9 \div 10 =$ _____   **k)** $0.6 \div 10 =$ _____   **l)** $0.3 \div 10 =$ _____

2. Record each quotient in the place-value chart.

   a) $7.8 \div 10$

   b) $0.4 \div 10$

   c) $14.9 \div 10$

   d) $593.6 \div 10$

   e) $0.8 \div 10$

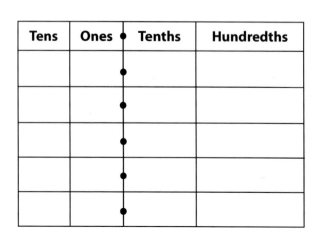

Tens	Ones	Tenths	Hundredths

Practice

1. Use mental math to divide.

   a) $1.6 \div 10 =$ _____   b) $0.4 \div 10 =$ _____   c) $825.3 \div 10 =$ _____

   d) $318.6 \div 10 =$ _____   e) $21.4 \div 10 =$ _____   f) $8.4 \div 10 =$ _____

   g) $60.8 \div 10 =$ _____   h) $504.6 \div 10 =$ _____   i) $0.7 \div 10 =$ _____

Use mental math to solve each problem.

2. A pile of ten 50¢ coins has a height of 19.5 mm.

   How thick is one 50¢ coin? _____

3. A case of 10 jars of peanut butter has a mass of 7.1 kg.

   What is the mass of 1 jar of peanut butter? _____

4. A row of 10 paper clips has a length of 3.2 dm.

   How long is 1 paper clip? _____

5. Terry divided a 1.5-L can of pineapple juice equally among 10 children.

   How much juice did each child get? _____

6. A table is 96.4 cm long. How many decimetres is that? _____

7. Patti rode her bike around the block 10 times. She rode a total of 8.7 km.

   What is the distance around the block? _____

Stretch Your Thinking

Sergio cut 4.6 metres of string into 10 equal pieces.
How long is each piece? Use as many different units as you can in your answer.

_____

_____

Interpreting Data

Quick Review

This table and each graph show the same data.

Trees Planted in Victory Park

Species	Number
Hickory	90
Oak	120
Willow	105
Birch	45

To find the **range** of the data, subtract the least value from the greatest.
$120 - 45 = 75$
The range is 75.

Pictograph	**Bar Graph**	**Circle Graph**

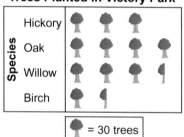

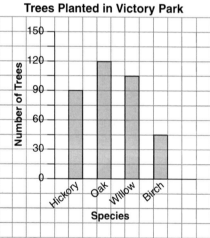

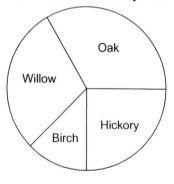

Try These ·

Use the data displayed above.

1. How many trees were planted in Victory Park? _____

2. What fraction of the trees was hickory? _____ Oak? _____

3. Half as many birch trees as which species were planted? _____

4. What does 🌳 on the pictograph represent? _____

1. Use the data in the table.

    a) How many people participated in the

    walk-a-thon? _____

    b) Which group had the most

    participants? _____

    c) What is the range of the data? _____

    Walk-A-Thon Participants

Group	Number
Girl Guides	171
Brownies	52
Boy Scouts	150
Cubs	54

2. The circle graph shows
    endangered animals in Canada.

    a) Estimate the fraction of
    animals that are birds. _____

    b) Which 2 categories make up about half
    of the animals?

    _____

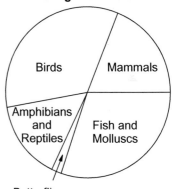

    Endangered Animals

3. This bar graph shows the length of time
    5 of the Prime Ministers of Canada were in
    office.

    a) Who was in office the longest time?

    _____

    The shortest time? _____

    b) Who was in office about 11 years longer

    than St. Laurent? _____

    c) What is the range of the data? _____

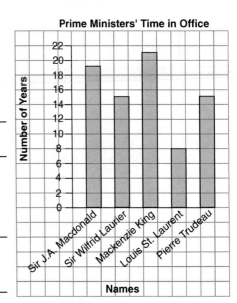

    Prime Ministers' Time in Office

Stretch Your Thinking

Lester B. Pearson was Prime Minister from April, 1963, to April, 1968.
How would you show this length of time on the bar graph in question 3 above?

Mean and Mode

Quick Review

➤ The **mean** is a number that represents the centre of a set of numbers.
Here is one way to find the mean of 7, 5, 5, 8, and 5.
Add: $7 + 5 + 5 + 8 + 5 = 30$
Divide by the number of numbers in the set.
There are 5 numbers in the set.
$30 \div 5 = 6$
The mean of 7, 5, 5, 8, and 5 is 6.

➤ The **mode** is the number that occurs most often in the data.
In the data above, the number 5 occurs most often.
The mode of 7, 5, 5, 8, and 5 is 5.

➤ Both the mean and the mode are sometimes called the **average**.

Try These

1. Calculate the mean of each set of data.

   a) 2, 6, 5, 7 _____   **b)** 1, 4, 9, 2, 9 _____

   c) $2, $5, $3, $8, $2 _____   **d)** 25, 10, 40 _____

   e) 5, 8, 12, 7, 3, 1 _____   **f)** 15, 15, 30 _____

2. Find the mode of each set of data.

   a) 3, 7, 6, 7, 6, 4, 6 _____   **b)** 8, 4, 8, 2, 4, 8, 7, 8 _____

   c) 1, 4, 1, 7, 1, 3, 1 _____   **d)** 3, 6, 3, 6, 8, 3, 3 _____

   e) 19, 15, 14, 15, 15 _____   **f)** 94, 16, 94, 83, 83, 94 _____

1. Calculate the mean of each set of data.

   a) 24, 16, 35, 52, 18 _____

   b) 150, 64, 73, 125 _____

   c) 20, 35, 14 _____

   d) 75, 70, 36, 51, 18 _____

2. Here are the masses of 6 dogs: 25 kg, 30 kg, 25 kg, 20 kg, 25 kg, 25 kg

   a) What is the mean mass? _____

   b) What is the mode of the masses? _____

3. Geraldo received these marks on 5 spelling tests: 100, 98, 97, 100, 100

   a) What is Geraldo's mean mark? _____

   b) What is the mode of his marks? _____

4. This table shows the heights and circumferences of 5 of Jack's trees.

   a) What is the mean height?

   _____

   b) What is the mean circumference?

   _____

Tree	Height (m)	Circumference (cm)
Oak	20	65
Elm	16	82
Maple	20	60
Birch	15	82
Poplar	9	21

   c) What is the mode of the heights? _____

   d) What is the mode of the circumferences? _____

5. Measure the height of 4 friends or family members.
   Record the heights in a table.

   Find the mean height.

   _____

Name	Height (cm)

Stretch Your Thinking

Jocelyn has 6 birds. Their mean age is 10. The mode of their ages is 8.

What might their ages be? _____

Drawing Bar Graphs

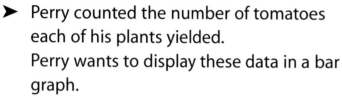
At Home
At School

Quick Review

➤ Perry counted the number of tomatoes each of his plants yielded.
Perry wants to display these data in a bar graph.

11, 11, 12, 12, 13, 14, 14, 14, 15, 16, 18, 19, 20, 21, 21, 22, 23, 25, 28, 29, 30, 32, 32, 33

There are too many pieces of data to graph each number separately.
So, Perry grouped the numbers into equal **intervals**.

Number of Tomatoes	Number of Plants
11–20	13
21–30	8
31–40	3

➤ Perry chose the scale 1 square represents 1 tomato plant.
He labelled the axes and drew a bar for each interval.
He gave the graph a title.

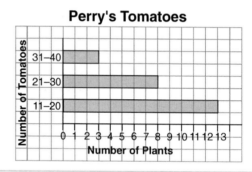

Perry's Tomatoes

Try These

1. The children in the Kindergarten class made paper chains.
The teacher recorded the number of links in each chain:
6, 8, 9, 9, 10, 12, 13, 13, 14, 16, 18, 19, 20, 22, 24, 24, 26, 27, 29
Arrange the data in intervals.
   a) Display the data in a table.
   b) Display the data in a bar graph.

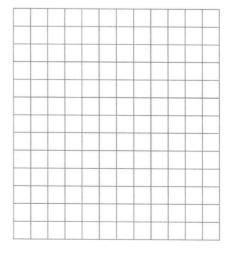

1. The students in Izzie's class recorded how long, in minutes, it takes them to get to school:

5, 5, 6, 7, 8, 9, 10, 10, 15, 15, 15, 17, 20, 20, 20, 20, 22, 23, 24, 25, 25, 25, 25, 25, 29

a) What is the mean of the data? _____

The mode? _____

b) Arrange the data into intervals. Make a table to display the data.

c) Display the data in a bar graph.

d) Write 2 things you can learn from the graph.

_____

_____

_____

Stretch Your Thinking

Suppose you want to group these data into intervals.

48, 72, 99, 100, 109, 132, 153, 184, 191, 201, 216, 284, 293, 299, 305, 320, 386, 391, 400, 410, 450, 486, 495, 499.

What intervals would you use? _____

_____

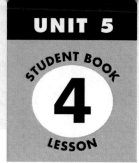
Line Graphs

At Home
At School

Quick Review

➤ A **line graph** can be used to show how data change over time.
This table and line graph show the enrolment at Bakerville Public
School from 1999 to 2004.

Enrolment at Bakerville Public School

Year	Number of Students
1999	420
2000	415
2001	412
2002	410
2003	402
2004	390

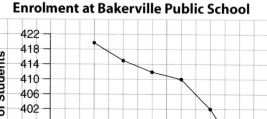

Enrolment at Bakerville Public School

On the line graph, each
point represents a number of students.
The data points are joined by line segments.
The line segments go down and to the right.
This shows that the enrolment at Bakerville Public School decreased
from 1999 to 2004.

Try These

1. This line graph shows the average
temperature in Howard's town over 6 months.
   a) What happened to the temperature from

   May to October? _____

   _____

   b) Which month was hottest? _____
   c) What would you expect the average
   temperature to be in November?

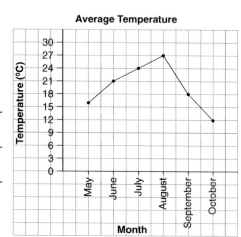

Average Temperature

_____

1. This table shows the number of children who took swimming lessons at a sports complex from 1998 to 2002.

Year	Number of Children
1998	2050
1999	2025
2000	2025
2001	2075
2002	3010

   a) Draw a line graph to display these data.

   b) Write 2 things this graph tells you.

   _____

   _____

   _____

   _____

   _____

   _____

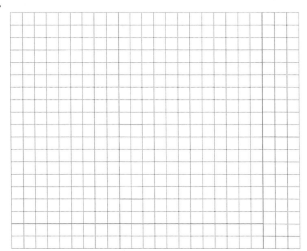

2. This line graph shows the growth of Basil's ponytail plant from January to May.

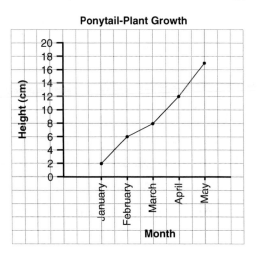

Ponytail-Plant Growth

   a) How tall was the plant in February?

   _____ April? _____

   b) In which month did the plant grow

   the most? _____

   c) How tall would you expect the plant to be by the end of June? Explain.

   _____

   _____

Name 3 situations for which you might display data on a line graph.

_____

_____

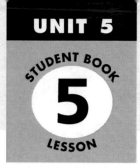
Interpreting Survey Results

At Home At School

Quick Review

Quincy wondered which shoe size is most common among Grade 5 students in his town.

Quincy cannot survey every Grade 5 student in the town, so he surveys a **sample** of 28 students in his school.
The table shows the results of Quincy's survey.

Quincy found out that size $4\frac{1}{2}$ is the most common shoe size.
The mode size is $4\frac{1}{2}$.

Quincy calculated the mean number of students for each shoe size to be 4.

Quincy decided that a sample of 28 students is biased (it does not truly represent the group of all Grade 5 students in the town).

Most Common Shoe Size

Size	Number of Students
3	3
$3\frac{1}{2}$	3
4	6
$4\frac{1}{2}$	8
5	4
$5\frac{1}{2}$	2
6	2

Try These

1. This graph shows the results of a student survey.
   a) What might the survey question have been?

   _____

   _____

   b) How many students were surveyed?

   _____

   c) What is the mode number of minutes

   spent on the phone each day? _____

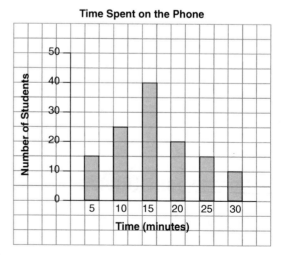
Time Spent on the Phone
Number of Students
Time (minutes)

1. Write a survey question and 4 possible answers for each topic.

   a) Homework _____

   _____

   b) Favourite super hero _____

   _____

2. a) Choose one of your survey
   questions from question 1.
   In the space to the right, draw a
   table where you could record
   possible answers to the question.
   Collect data from at least 10 people.
   Record the data in your table.

   b) Write 2 things you learned from
   the survey.

   _____

   _____

3. Look at the tally chart.
   How many people were surveyed? _____
   How might the sample have been biased?

Should Grade 5 Students Do More Homework?	
Yes	|||
No	₩₩ ₩₩ ₩₩ ₩₩ ₩₩

   _____

   _____

Stretch Your Thinking

1. For each survey question, describe an appropriate sample group.
   a) Should students go to school all year long?

   _____

   b) What is your favourite make of car?

   _____

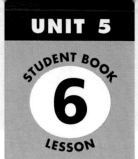
Bias in Displaying Data

At Home
At School

Quick Review

In a survey, 500 dentists were asked to choose between 2 brands of dental floss.

The results are displayed in 2 different graphs.

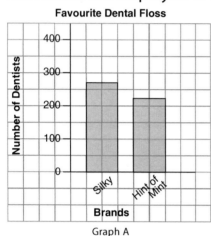

Graph A

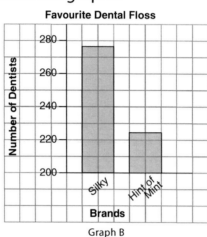

Graph B

The difference between the numbers of dentists who chose Silky brand or Hint of Mint brand is not very great.

Graph B makes it appear that 3 times as many dentists chose Silky over Hint of Mint. Graph B is **biased**.

Try These

a) Which graph shows the data with bias? _____

b) In what way is it biased?

_____

_____

_____

_____

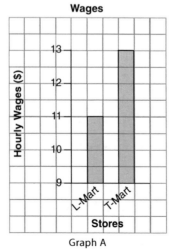

Graph A

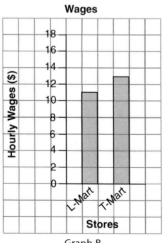

Graph B

Practice

1. The table and the graphs show the results of a survey.

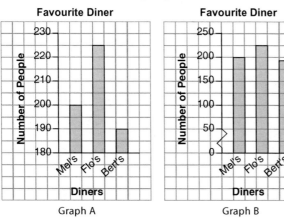

Graph A

Graph B

Diner	Number of People
Mel's	200
Flo's	225
Bert's	190

a) How many people were surveyed? _____

b) What is the range of the data? _____

c) Which graph makes the range appear greater than it really is? Explain.

_____

_____

2. Suppose you are advertising Smoothie Peanut Butter. Which graph would you use? Explain.

_____

_____

_____

_____

_____

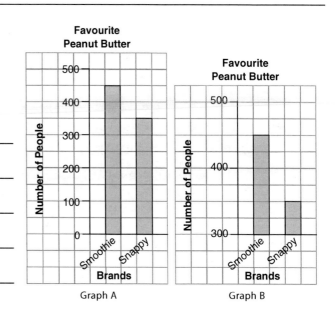

Graph A

Graph B

Stretch Your Thinking

What advice would you give to people so that they will not be misled by biased graphs? _____

_____

Measuring Time

At Home
At School

Quick Review

➤ This clock shows a time of
25 minutes 40 seconds after 9 o'clock.
In **SI notation**, we write 09:25:40.

➤ There are 60 seconds in one minute.
It takes 60 s for the second hand to move all the way around the clock.

We can round time to the nearest minute.

When there are less than 30 s,
round back to the full minute.

When there are 30 s or more,
round forward to the next full minute.

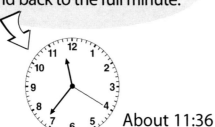 About 11:36

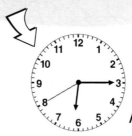 About 06:15

➤ The circled date is April 25th, 2005.
April is the 4th month of the year.
In SI notation, we write: 2005 04 25.

April 2005

S	M	T	W	T	F	S
					1	2
3	4	5	6	7	8	9
10	11	12	13	14	15	16
17	18	19	20	21	22	23
24	(25)	26	27	28	29	30

Try These

1. In SI notation, write the exact time and the time to the nearest minute.

a)

b)

c)

Practice

1. Draw the hands on each clock to show the time.

   a)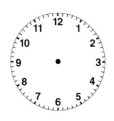
   01:10:15

   b)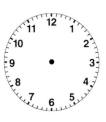
   09:45:29

   c)
   11:29:38

   d)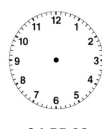
   04:55:03

2. Write each date in SI notation.

   a) December 8, 2009 _____

   b) February 8, 1941 _____

   c) today's date _____

   d) the date 2 months from today _____

3. Write each date in words.

   a) 2005 09 24 _____

   b) 2010 11 06 _____

4. Take turns with a partner.
   Estimate how long it will take you to do each activity.
   Have your partner time you, to the nearest second, as you do the activity.

	Activity	Estimated Time	Actual Time
a)	Sing "O Canada"		
b)	Write your name 10 times		
c)	Say the 12-times table		
d)	Do 10 jumping jacks		

Stretch Your Thinking

Stanley left home at 08:10:17 and arrived at school at 8:35:21. How long did it take Stanley to get to school?

_____

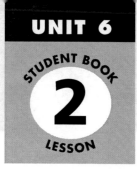

UNIT 6

STUDENT BOOK 2 LESSON

Exploring Time and Distance

Quick Review

Speed is a measure of how fast an object is moving.
Olivia's remote control car travels 150 cm every second.
At this speed, it will go:

• 150 cm in 1 s
• 300 cm in 2 s
• 450 cm in 3 s, and so on.

We can show this:

➤ In a table

Time (s)	Distance (cm)
1	150
2	300
3	450
4	600

➤ On a graph

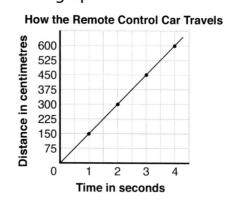

How the Remote Control Car Travels

Try These

1. A toy robot travels 3 m every minute.
   At this speed, how far will it go in each time period?

   a) 1 min _____   **b)** 2 min _____   **c)** 5 min _____   **d)** 10 min _____

2. A snail travels 20 cm in one minute and 40 cm in 2 minutes.
   At this speed, how far will the snail travel in each time period?

   a) 3 min _____   **b)** 4 min _____

   c) 5 min _____   **d)** 8 min _____

3. Jethro jogs 1 km every 7 min.
   How long will it take him to jog 9 km? _____

78

1. A train travels 75 km every hour.
   a) Complete the table to show how far the train travels in 5 hours.
   b) Suppose a trip is a total distance of 600 km. How long will it take the train to make the trip?

   _____

Time (h)	Distance (km)

2. A tour bus travels 60 km in one hour.
   At this speed, how far does it travel in each time period?

   a) 5 min _____   b) 10 min _____   c) 15 min _____   d) 30 min _____

3. Look at the graph.
   a) How far does the truck travel in 2 hours? _____
   b) How long does it take the truck to travel 360 km? _____
   c) Suppose the truck travelled for 7 hours at the same speed.

   How far would it travel? _____

   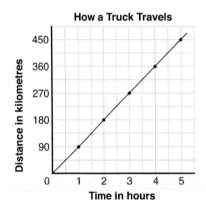

   How a Truck Travels

4. It takes about 15 minutes to walk 1 km.

   At this speed, about how far could you walk in 2 hours? _____
   Show your work.

   _____

Suppose an express train travels 90 km every hour.
How far would it travel in $5\frac{1}{2}$ hours?

_____

_____

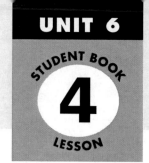
Estimating and Counting Money

Quick Review

Here is a collection of money.

Here is one way to count the money:

➤ Sort the bills and coins into groups and then count them.

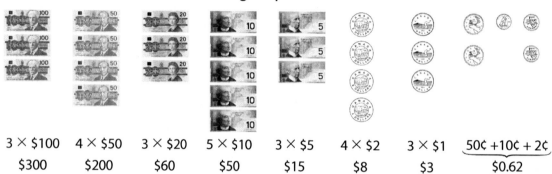

3 × $100	4 × $50	3 × $20	5 × $10	3 × $5	4 × $2	3 × $1	50¢ +10¢ + 2¢
$300	$200	$60	$50	$15	$8	$3	$0.62

Then, add: $300 + $200 + $60 + $50 + $15 + $8 + $3 + $0.62 = $636.62

Try These

1. Estimate, then count.

Estimate: _____ Amount: _____

2. Draw pictures. Show $367.82 using the fewest bills and coins.

Practice

Use play money when it helps.
1. Show 3 different ways to make $745.32.

2. Make each amount using the fewest bills and coins.
   Record the numbers of bills and coins in the table.

	$100	$50	$20	$10	$5	$2	$1	25¢	10¢	5¢	1¢
$126.38											
$829.92											
$408.69											

3. Donald has 7 bills.
   He has $350. What bills could Donald have?
   Give 3 different answers.

_____

_____

_____

Stretch Your Thinking

Simone has 20 bills. One-fifth of the bills are hundreds, $\frac{1}{4}$ of them are fifties, $\frac{1}{10}$ of them are $20s. The rest of the bills are tens.
Simone has $780 altogether. How many of each kind of bill does she have?

_____

_____

Making Change

Quick Review

Emma bought a cordless phone for $57.65.
She paid for it with 1 $50 bill and 1 $20 bill.

Here's how the clerk made change for Emma:
"That's $57.65 . . .

$57.75   . . . $58.00   . . . $60.00   . . . $70.00"

"That's $12.35 in change."

Emma estimates to check she got the correct change.

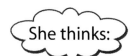 She thinks: "The phone cost about $58. I got about $12 in change.
$58 + $12 is $70.
That's right."

Try These

1. Draw pictures to show the change for each purchase.

   a) Aki bought a cell phone for $72.49. He paid for it with a $100 bill.

   b) Millie bought a scooter for $62.35. She paid for it with 4 $20 bills.

   c) Sophia bought a beanbag chair for $59.42. She paid for it with 2 $50 bills.

   d) Troy bought a pair of runners for $85.09. He paid for it with 4 $20 bills
   and 1 $10 bill.

1. Draw pictures to show the change for each purchase.

Purchase	Money Used to Pay	Change
$68.99	50 50	
$58.65	100	
$49.75	20 20 20	

2. Sudhir bought a telescope for $75.98. He got $4.02 in change.

   a) How much money did Sudhir give the clerk? _____

   b) What bills might he have given the clerk? Give 2 answers.

   _____

3. Audrey has $72 to spend on DVDs. Each DVD costs $23.19.

   a) How many DVDs can she buy? _____

   b) How much change will she get? _____

   c) What coins might Audrey get in change?

   _____

4. Alonzo paid for a $91.57 purchase with a $100 bill. He got 3 pennies, 4 dimes, and 5 toonies in change. Did he get the correct change? Explain.

   _____

   _____

Stretch Your Thinking

Evelyn bought a sweater for $38.63. The clerk gave her $12 in change.
How much money had Evelyn given the clerk? Explain.

Capacity

Quick Review

The amount that a container can hold is its capacity.
Capacity is measured in litres (L) and millilitres (mL). 1000 mL = 1 L
Which container has the greatest capacity? The least capacity?

A   B   C

Container A has a capacity of 1.36 L. This is 1.36 × 1000 mL = 1360 mL.
Container B has a capacity of 750 mL.
Container C has a capacity of 1.5 L. This is 1.5 × 1000 mL = 1500 mL.
Container C has the greatest capacity.
Container B has the least capacity.

Try These

1. Write each capacity in millilitres.

    a) 3.25 L _____   **b)** 7.89 L _____   **c)** 1.48 L _____

    d) 0.5 L _____   **e)** 0.2 L _____   **f)** 1.03 L _____

2. Order these capacities from least to greatest.

    a) 1.65 L, 1024 mL, 1.7 L _____

    b) 0.85 L, 1.3 L, 1146 mL _____

3. Would you use millilitres or litres to measure each capacity?

    a)   **b)**   **c)**

_____   _____   _____

Use a calculator when it helps.

1. Order these capacities from least to greatest.

   a) 1.5 L, 1400 mL, 1.56 L _____

   b) 2000 mL, 1.8 L, 2.5 L _____

   c) 6 L, 6200 mL, 3.9 L _____

2. Use <, >, or = to make each statement true.

   a) 500 mL _____ 5 L   **b)** 750 mL _____ 1 L   **c)** 4.35 L _____ 1000 mL

   d) 149 mL _____ 1 L   **e)** 3.5 L _____ 3500 mL   **f)** 1.3 L _____ 1100 mL

3. Find 5 items at home with capacities shown in millilitres or litres.
   List the items and their capacities in order from least to greatest.

   _____

   _____

4. Penelope says that a 7-L container has a greater capacity than fifteen 500-mL

   containers. Is she right? Explain. _____

   _____

5. Jerry carries water in a 3-L jug to fill his birdbath.
   If the birdbath holds 8 L of water, how many trips will Jerry have to make to

   fill the birdbath? Explain. _____

   _____

   _____

Stretch Your Thinking

Julianne's recipe for chicken potpie calls for 750 mL of broth.
Julianne is making a triple batch of potpie.
How much broth will she use?
Give your answer in millilitres and litres.

Volume

At Home
At School

Quick Review

The **volume** of an object is a measure of the space it takes up.

The length of each edge of this centimetre cube is 1 cm.

A centimetre cube has a volume of one **cubic centimetre** (**1 cm³**). We can use centimetre cubes to measure volume.

➤ This rectangular prism has 3 rows of 4 cubes, or 12 cubes. The volume is 12 cubic centimetres, or 12 cm³.

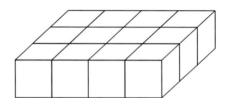

➤ This solid has 6 cubes in the bottom layer and 3 cubes in the top layer. The volume is 9 cubic centimetres, or 9 cm³.

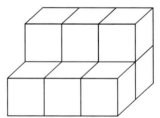

Try These

Use centimetre cubes to help.

1. Each prism is made with centimetre cubes. Find the volume of each prism.

   a)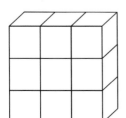

   b)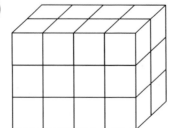

   c)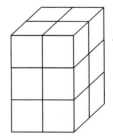

   _____   _____   _____

2. Order the solids in question 1 from least to greatest volume. _____

1. Use centimetre cubes.
   Build 3 different rectangular prisms with volume 12 cm³.
   Describe each prism.

   a) _____

   b) _____

   c) _____

2. Each solid is made with centimetre cubes.
   Estimate the volume of each solid. Then, find each volume.

   a)   b)   c)

   Estimate: _____   Estimate: _____   Estimate: _____

   Volume: _____   Volume: _____   Volume: _____

3. Order the solids in question 2 from greatest to least volume. _____

4. How many different rectangular prisms with a volume of 11 cm³ can you
   build with centimetre cubes? Explain.

   _____

   _____

Stretch Your Thinking

Find a small box. Estimate its volume in cubic centimetres.
Use centimetre cubes to find the volume of the box.

a) How did you find the volume of the box?

   _____

   _____

b) Is the volume exact or approximate? Explain.

   _____

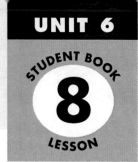

Relating Capacity and Volume

Quick Review

You can find the volume of an object by measuring the amount of water **displaced** or moved by the object.

There are 250 mL of water in the container.

The prism has raised the water level to 300 mL.

300 mL – 250 mL = 50 mL
The prism displaced 50 mL of water.

1 mL = 1 cm³
50 mL = 50 cm³
So, the volume of the prism is 50 cm³.

Try These

1. What is the volume of each object?

a)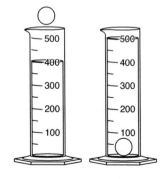

b)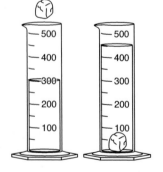

c)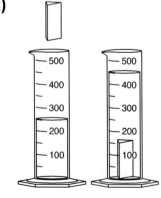

_____ _____ _____

1. You will need a measuring cup marked in millimetres, water, and 6 objects that will sink.
   Find the volume of each object. Complete the chart.

Object	Water Level Without Object	Water Level With Object	Amount of Water Displaced	Volume of the Object

2. Order the objects you used in question 1 from least to greatest volume.

_____

_____

_____

Stretch Your Thinking

Nancy filled a measuring cup with water to the 450-mL mark.
She dropped 4 golf balls into the cup.
The water level rose to the 650-mL mark.
What is the volume of one golf ball? Explain.

_____

_____

_____

_____

Measuring Mass

Quick Review

We use milligrams (mg), grams (g), and kilograms (kg) to measure mass.

➤ Heavy objects are measured in kilograms.

1000 g = 1 kg

➤ Light objects are measured in grams.

1000 mg = 1 g

➤ Very light objects are measured in milligrams.

Try These

1. Would you use milligrams, grams, or kilograms to measure the mass of each object?

a)

b)

c)

d)

e)

f)

1. Complete each statement.

   a) 2 kg = _____ g **b)** 7 g = _____ mg **c)** 5000 g = _____ kg

   d) 2000 mg = _____ g **e)** 4000 g = _____ kg **f)** 8000 mg = _____ g

2. Darryl bought a banana, a peach, and a melon.
   Together, the banana and the peach have $\frac{1}{2}$ the mass of the melon.
   The mass of the melon is 700 g.
   a) What is the combined mass of the banana and the peach? _____
   b) The peach is 10 g heavier than the banana.

   What is the mass of the peach? _____ The banana? _____

3. A pumpkin seed has a mass of about 250 mg.
   About how many pumpkin seeds would it take to make a total mass of 10 g?
   Explain how you know.

   _____

   _____

   _____

4. Small nails cost $1.89 per kilogram.
   Joseph needs 500 g of small nails to build a dog house.
   How much will Joseph pay for the nails?

   _____

   _____

Stretch Your Thinking

Bananas cost $0.98 per kilogram.
About how many 170-g bananas can you buy for 1 dollar?

_____

_____

_____

_____

Exploring Large Masses

At Home
At School

Quick Review

The **tonne** (**t**) is a large unit of mass.
The tonne is used to measure very heavy objects.

 1000 kg = 1 t

The mass of this
whale is about 1 t.

The mass of this
tractor is about 7 t.

Try These

1. Would you use milligrams, grams, kilograms, or tonnes to measure each mass?

a)

b)

c)

_____

_____

_____

d)

e)

f)

_____

_____

_____

1. Complete. Use a calculator when it helps.

   a) 7 t = _____ kg **b)** 3 t = _____ kg **c)** 1250 kg = _____ t

   d) 1400 kg = _____ t **e)** 5.2 t = _____ kg **f)** 2100 kg = _____ t

2. Choose the best estimate for each mass.

   a)    **b)**    **c)**

        23 mg 23 g 23 kg   600 kg 800 kg 6 t   144 mg 144 g 144 kg

3. Estimate the mass of each item in milligrams, grams, kilograms, or tonnes.

   a) a watermelon seed _____ **b)** a newborn baby _____

   c) a bag of 75 jelly beans _____ **d)** a transport truck _____

4. Order these masses from least to greatest.

   a) 600 g, 6 kg, 3000 mg _____

   b) 1 t, 3000 kg, 2.5 t _____

5. Which mass is closest to 2 tonnes? How do you know?
   2100 kg   3000 kg   1900 kg

   _____

   _____

Stretch Your Thinking

About how many boxes of this cereal
would it take to equal 1 t?

_____

Coordinate Systems

Quick Review

Here are 2 kinds of **coordinate systems**.

➤ On a map, a pair of coordinates refers to a square.

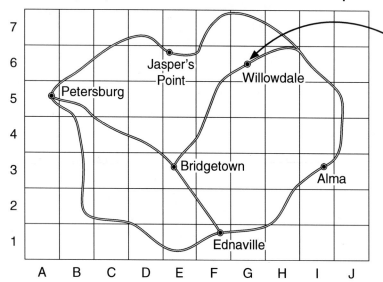

The town of Willowdale is in G6.

➤ On a grid, a pair of coordinates refers to a point where the grid lines cross.

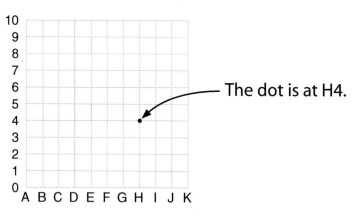

The dot is at H4.

Try These

1. Use the map above. Write the coordinates of each town.

   a) Jasper's Point _____   **b)** Alma _____   **c)** Ednaville _____   **d)** Petersburg _____

2. Use the grid above. Mark a point at each pair of coordinates using the colour named.

   a) F7, green   **b)** A9, yellow   **c)** J3, red   **d)** G8, blue

Practice

1. **a)** Mark a point at each pair of coordinates:
   B1   E6   F1   I6

   b) Connect the points to form a quadrilateral.

   c) Name the quadrilateral. _____

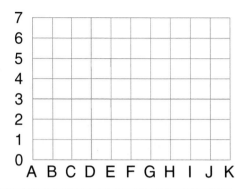

2. This map shows the locations of 6 buried treasures. Write the coordinates of each item.

   a) Gold _____   **b)** Silver _____

   c) Crown _____   **d)** Coins _____

   e) Rubies _____   **f)** Pearls _____

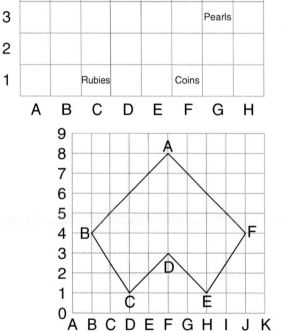

3. Write the coordinates of each vertex of the figure.

   A _____   B _____   C _____

   D _____   E _____   F _____

Stretch Your Thinking

Use the coordinates of each letter to decode the message below.

___ ___ ___ ___
D4   E6   A2   E2

___ ___ ___ ___ ___
D4   E6   F5   A5   B1

___ ___ ___ ___ ___
B1   A5   C7   B1   A5

	A	B	C	D	E	F
7	B	I	N	V	P	U
6	F	Q	D	I	A	J
5	E	G	P	F	W	K
4	O	R	C	M	Y	Q
3	L	X	L	R	O	U
2	T	Y	D	C	H	X
1	Z	S	J	G	W	V

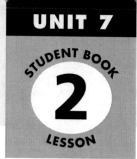

Transformations

 At Home At School

Quick Review

A translation, a reflection, and a rotation are transformations.

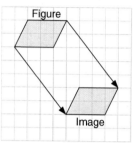

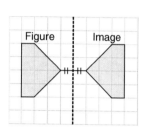

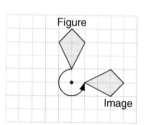

A translation slides a figure along a straight line.

A reflection is a flip. The figure and its image face opposite ways.

A rotation is a turn. The figure and its image may face different ways.

When you translate, reflect, or rotate a figure, the figure and its image are congruent.

Try These

1. Name each transformation.

a)

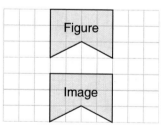

_____

b)

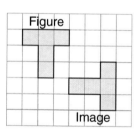

c)

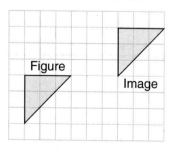

d)

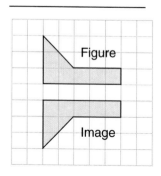

_____

_____

1. Draw the image of this figure after
   each transformation.
   Label each image with the letter shown.
   A – a translation of 8 squares right
   and 3 squares down
   B – a reflection in the broken line
   C – a $\frac{1}{4}$ turn counterclockwise
   about the dot.

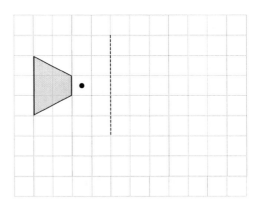

2. Name the transformation that moves the figure to each image.

   a) Image A _____

   b) Image B _____

   c) Image C _____

   d) Image D _____

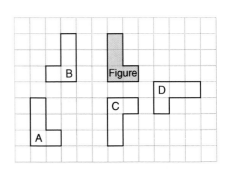

Use three transformations.
Move Figure A to coincide with Figure B.
Describe the transformations.

_____

_____

_____

_____

_____

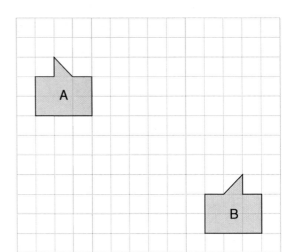

Congruent Figures

Quick Review

Congruent figures have the same shape and size.
These quadrilaterals are congruent.

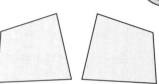

Here are 2 ways to check if figures are congruent.

➤ Fold the paper.
The figures are congruent if
they coincide.

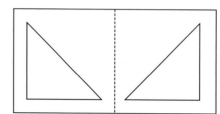

➤ Using tracing paper.
Trace one of the figures.
Place the tracing on top of the other figure.
The figures are congruent if they coincide.

Try These

1. Are these pairs of figures congruent?

   a)

   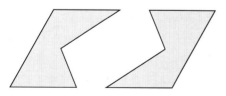

   _____

   b)

   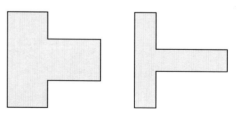

   _____

   c)

   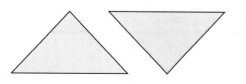

   _____

   d)

   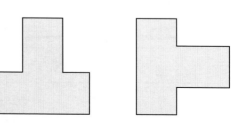

   _____

1. **a)** Draw 2 congruent hexagons. Label them A and B.
   Draw a hexagon that is not congruent to hexagons A and B.
   Label it C.

   b) How do you know hexagons A and B are congruent?

   _____

   c) How do you know hexagon C is not congruent to hexagons A and B?

   _____

2. Divide each figure into 4 congruent parts.

   a)   **b)**   **c)**   **d)**

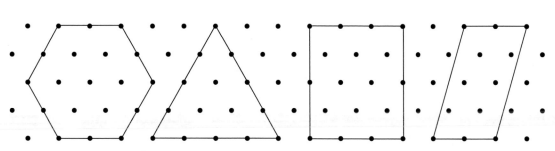

Find a different way to divide each square into 16 congruent parts.

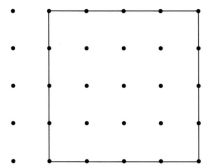 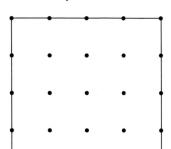 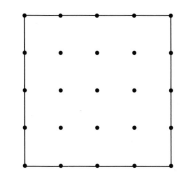

Line Symmetry

Quick Review

A line of symmetry is a mirror line.
It divides a figure into 2 congruent parts.
A **symmetrical** figure has one or more lines of symmetry.

Here is one way to make a symmetrical figure.

➤ Fold a piece of paper.
Draw a figure.
Cut out the figure.

fold ➜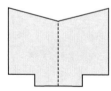

➤ Unfold the paper.
The fold line is a line of symmetry.

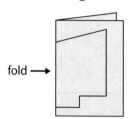

Try These

1. Find the figures that have line symmetry.
   Draw the lines of symmetry.

a)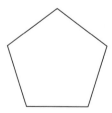

b)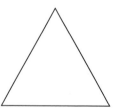

c)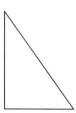

d)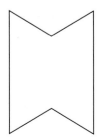

e)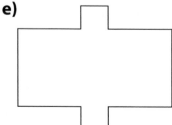

f)

1. One-half of a symmetrical figure is shown.
   Complete the figure.

   a)    b)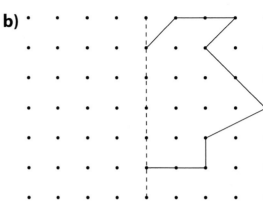

2. Draw one-half of a design on one side of the mirror line.
   Then, draw the mirror image of the design on the other side.

   a) 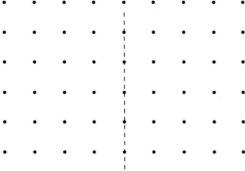   b)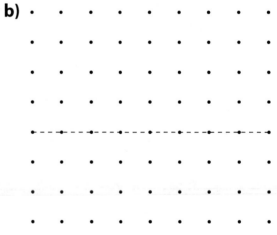

Stretch Your Thinking

One-quarter of a symmetrical design
is shown. Complete the design.

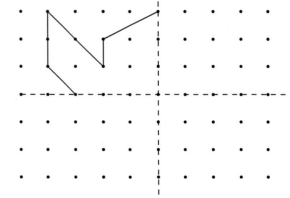

Exploring Tiling

Quick Review

A **tiling pattern** covers a surface with figures.
There are no gaps or overlaps.

A tiling pattern with all figures congruent is a **tessellation**.

The hexagon was rotated a $\frac{1}{2}$ turn clockwise about the dot.
The figure formed by the hexagon and its rotation image was translated 3 squares right.
To get the second row, the figure was reflected.

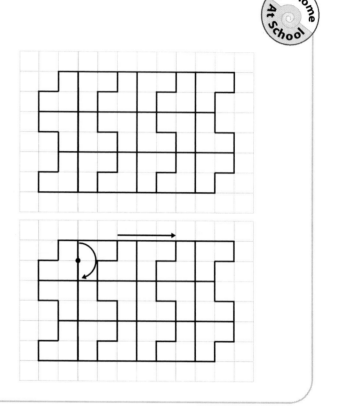

Try These

1. a) Transform the figure to create a tessellation.

   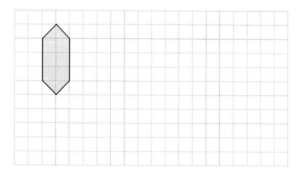

   b) Describe the transformations you used.

   _____

   _____

   _____

   _____

1. **a)** Draw a figure on the grid paper.
       Transform the figure to create a tiling pattern.

    b) Describe the transformations you used.

       _____

       _____

       _____

Stretch Your Thinking

Find an example of a tiling pattern
in an old magazine.
Cut it out and glue it in the space
to the right.
Describe the transformations
that were used to create the pattern.

_____

_____

_____

_____

_____

Equivalent Fractions

Quick Review

  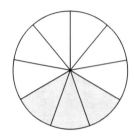 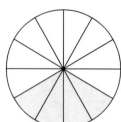

$\frac{1}{3}$ of the circle is shaded.

$\frac{2}{6}$ of the circle is shaded.

$\frac{3}{9}$ of the circle is shaded.

$\frac{4}{12}$ of the circle is shaded.

➤ $\frac{1}{3}, \frac{2}{6}, \frac{3}{9},$ and $\frac{4}{12}$ represent the same amount. They are equivalent fractions.

➤ There are patterns in the equivalent fractions.

The numerators are multiples of the least numerator, 1.

$$\frac{1}{3}, \frac{2}{6}, \frac{3}{9}, \frac{4}{12}$$

The denominators are multiples of the least denominator, 3.

Try These

Write 3 equivalent fractions for each picture.

1.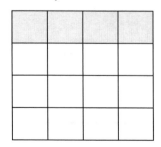

2.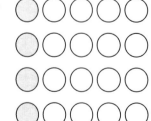

3.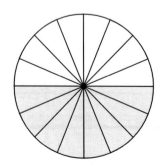

_____   _____   _____

Practice

1. Write 2 equivalent fractions for each fraction.
   Use the diagram to help.

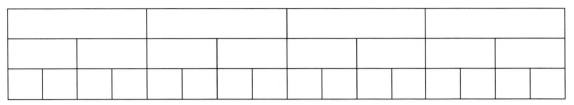

   a) $\frac{1}{4}$ _____ **b)** $\frac{2}{4}$ _____ **c)** $\frac{3}{4}$ _____ **d)** $\frac{4}{4}$ _____

2. Write as many equivalent fractions as you can for each picture.

   a)

   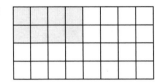

   b)

   △ △ △
   △ ▲ △
   ▲ △ △
   △ △ ▲

   c)

   _____   _____   _____

3. Draw a picture to show each pair of equivalent fractions.
   a) $\frac{2}{5}$ and $\frac{6}{15}$ **b)** $\frac{4}{6}$ and $\frac{16}{24}$

Stretch Your Thinking

Find as many equivalent fractions as you can
for the shaded section of this hundredths grid.

_____

Fractions and Mixed Numbers

Quick Review

Suppose 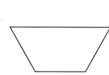 = 1 whole   Then, $\bigtriangledown$ = $\frac{1}{2}$

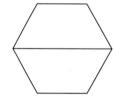

This arrangement shows $\frac{7}{2}$ or $3\frac{1}{2}$.

$\frac{7}{2}$ and $3\frac{1}{2}$ are equivalent.

$\frac{1}{2}$ is a **proper fraction**.

$\frac{7}{2}$ is an **improper fraction**.

$3\frac{1}{2}$ is a **mixed number**.

Try These

1. Write an improper fraction and a mixed number for each picture.

a) 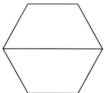   b) 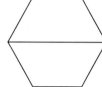   c)

_____   _____   _____

d)    e) 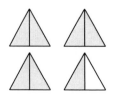   f)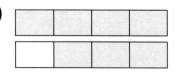

_____   _____   _____

Practice

1. Draw a picture to show each mixed number.
   Then, write an equivalent improper fraction.
   a) $2\frac{7}{8}$ pizzas

   ____

   b) $4\frac{1}{4}$ sandwiches

   ____

2. Draw a picture to show each improper fraction.
   Then, write an equivalent mixed number.
   a) $\frac{9}{4}$ circles

   ____

   b) $\frac{9}{5}$ rectangles

   ____

Stretch Your Thinking

Stella watched 9 half-hour programs on TV last week.
Mort watched 3 one-hour programs. Who spent more time watching TV last week?

____

____

Comparing and Ordering Fractions

Quick Review

Here are some ways to compare and order fractions.

➤ To order $\frac{1}{2}$, $\frac{4}{5}$, and $\frac{2}{3}$:
Draw 3 number lines.

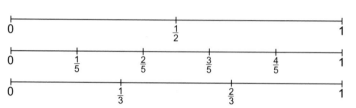

From least to greatest:
$\frac{1}{2}$, $\frac{2}{3}$, $\frac{4}{5}$

➤ To compare $\frac{4}{5}$ and $\frac{7}{10}$:

Find equivalent fractions with tenths.

$\frac{4}{5} = \frac{8}{10}$

$\frac{8}{10} > \frac{7}{10}$, or $\frac{4}{5} > \frac{7}{10}$

Try These

1. **a)** Show thirds on the first number line.
Show fourths on the second line.
Show sixths on the third line.

b) Use the number lines to order these fractions from least to greatest: $\frac{2}{3}$, $\frac{3}{4}$, $\frac{2}{6}$.

_____

Practice

1. Use the strips below to order these fractions from least to greatest: $\frac{3}{4}, \frac{5}{6}, \frac{5}{8}$

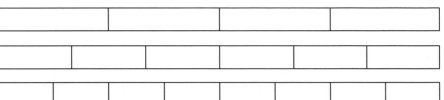

_____

2. Use equivalent fractions to compare the fractions in each pair.
   Write >, <, or =.

   a) $\frac{3}{4}$ _____ $\frac{7}{8}$ **b)** $\frac{1}{2}$ _____ $\frac{4}{10}$ **c)** $\frac{2}{3}$ _____ $\frac{5}{9}$ **d)** $\frac{3}{5}$ _____ $\frac{2}{10}$

3. Which fraction in each pair is greater? Tell how you know.
   a) $\frac{3}{8}$ or $\frac{5}{8}$

   _____

   b) $\frac{4}{9}$ or $\frac{4}{7}$

   _____

   c) $\frac{6}{12}$ or $\frac{7}{24}$

   _____

4. Name 4 fractions that are less than $\frac{2}{3}$.
   Each fraction should have a different denominator.

   _____

Stretch Your Thinking

1. Write a fraction to make each statement true.

   a) $\frac{7}{8} <$ _____   **b)** $\frac{99}{100} >$ _____   **c)** _____ $< \frac{1}{4}$ **d)** _____ > 5

Relating Fractions to Decimals

Quick Review

➤ You can write fractions with denominators of 10 and 100 as decimals.
$\frac{6}{10}$ is 6 tenths or 0.6. $\frac{9}{100}$ is 9 hundredths or 0.09.

➤ If a fraction does not have a denominator of 10 or 100, try to find an equivalent fraction that does.

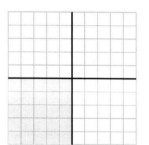

$\frac{1}{5}$ is equivalent to $\frac{2}{10}$.

$\frac{2}{10}$ is 2 tenths, or 0.2.

$\frac{1}{5}$ and 0.2 are equivalent.

$\frac{1}{4}$ is equivalent to $\frac{25}{100}$.

$\frac{25}{100}$ is 25 hundredths or 0.25.

$\frac{1}{4}$ and 0.25 are equivalent.

Try These
. . . .

1. Write a fraction and a decimal to describe the shaded part of each grid.

    a)

    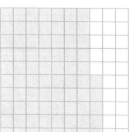

    _____

    b)

    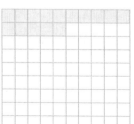

    _____

    c)

    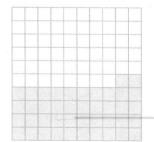

    _____

1. Colour each grid to show the fraction.
   Then, write the fraction as a decimal.

   a) 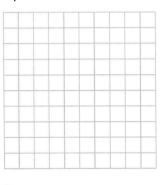   **b)** 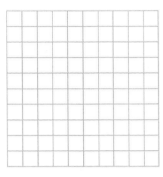   **c)**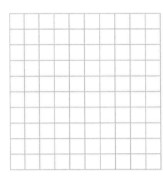

   $\frac{3}{4}$ _____ $\frac{8}{100}$ _____ $\frac{3}{5}$ _____

2. Use >, <, or = to make each statement true.

   a) $\frac{1}{4}$ _____ $\frac{25}{100}$ **b)** 0.07 _____ $\frac{2}{100}$ **c)** 0.2 _____ $\frac{20}{100}$

   d) $\frac{2}{5}$ _____ $\frac{30}{100}$ **e)** $\frac{3}{4}$ _____ $\frac{95}{100}$ **f)** $2\frac{1}{2}$ _____ 2.5

3. Write two equivalent fractions for each decimal.

   a) 0.25 _____   **b)** 0.4 _____

   c) 1.6 _____   **d)** 0.75 _____

4. Write each fraction as a decimal.

   a) $3\frac{1}{2}$ _____   **b)** $\frac{16}{20}$ _____   **c)** $\frac{7}{5}$ _____

   d) $\frac{36}{100}$ _____   **e)** $2\frac{3}{4}$ _____   **f)** $\frac{4}{5}$ _____

Write a decimal that is close in value to each of these fractions:

$\frac{1}{3}$ _____ $\frac{2}{3}$ _____ $\frac{1}{8}$ _____ $\frac{5}{8}$ _____

Fraction and Decimal Benchmarks

Quick Review

➤ Which fraction benchmark is $\frac{6}{9}$ closest to?

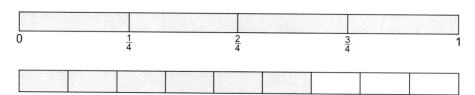

$\frac{6}{9}$ is greater than $\frac{1}{2}$ and less than $\frac{3}{4}$.
It is closer to $\frac{3}{4}$.

➤ Which decimal benchmark is 0.3 closest to?

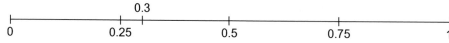

0.3 is greater than 0.25 and less than 0.5.
It is closer to 0.25.

Try These

1. Which benchmark is each fraction closest to?

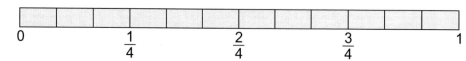

a) $\frac{11}{12}$ _____   b) $\frac{5}{12}$ _____   c) $\frac{1}{12}$ _____   d) $\frac{10}{12}$ _____

2. Which benchmark is each decimal closest to?

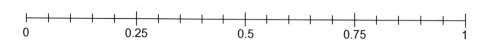

a) 0.6 _____   b) 0.95 _____   c) 0.1 _____   d) 0.35 _____

1. Colour each hundredths chart to show the decimal.
   Tell which benchmark each decimal is closest to.

   a)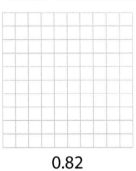

   0.82

   Closest to _____

   b)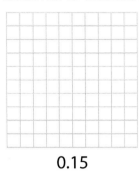

   0.15

   Closest to _____

   c)

   0.73

   Closest to _____

2. a) Place $\frac{18}{20}$ and $\frac{3}{10}$ on this number line.

   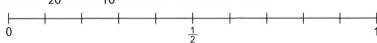

   b) Tell which benchmark each fraction is closest to:

   $\frac{18}{20}$ _____ $\frac{3}{10}$ _____

   c) Place a fraction on the number line which is greater than $\frac{1}{2}$ and

   less than $\frac{3}{4}$. _____

3. a) Darryl's water bottle is less than $\frac{1}{4}$ full.
   Write a fraction that might tell how full it is. _____

   b) Benita's water bottle is more than $\frac{1}{2}$ full and less than $\frac{3}{4}$ full.

   Write a fraction that might tell how full it is. _____

4. Complete each statement.

   a) 0.78 is between the benchmarks _____ and _____, but closer to _____.

   b) 0.31 is between the benchmarks _____ and _____, but closer to _____.

Stretch Your Thinking

Name 5 decimals that are between 1 and 1.25 but closer to 1.

Relating Fractions to Division

Quick Review

➤ Wayne has 5 fruit bars to share among 3 people.
How much will each person get?

Divide.

Five fruit bars shared among 3 people
is written as $5 \div 3$, or $\frac{5}{3}$.

$$3\overline{)5} \\ 1\text{ R}2$$

Each person gets 1 whole fruit bar.
There are 2 left over.
Divide each leftover fruit bar in thirds.

There are 6 thirds.
Each person gets 2 thirds
of the leftover fruit bars.
So, each person gets $1\frac{2}{3}$ fruit bars.

➤ Any division statement can be written as a fraction.
$5 \div 3 = \frac{5}{3} = 1\frac{2}{3}$

Try These

1. Write each division statement as a fraction.

   a) $3 \div 7$ _____

   b) $4 \div 6$ _____

   c) $5 \div 9$ _____

   d) $8 \div 6$ _____

   e) $10 \div 4$ _____

   f) $12 \div 5$ _____

2. Write each fraction as a division statement.

   a) $\frac{4}{5}$ _____

   b) $\frac{12}{8}$ _____

   c) $\frac{15}{4}$ _____

   d) $\frac{1}{6}$ _____

   e) $\frac{3}{4}$ _____

   f) $\frac{26}{3}$ _____

Draw a picture to solve each problem. Show all your work.

1. How many pears would each person get if 14 pears are shared among 4 people?

_____

2. Salvador baked 3 apple tarts.
He shared them equally among 4 friends.
How much did each friend get?

_____

_____

_____

3. Eight people won $200. How much will each person's share be?

_____

Stretch Your Thinking . . . .

Each of 4 people got $5\frac{3}{4}$ cookies.
How many cookies were shared?

_____

_____

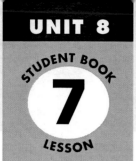

Estimating Products and Quotients

Quick Review

➤ A movie ticket costs $8.45.
Estimate the cost of 4 tickets.

Estimate: $8.45 × 4

$8.45 is about $8.50.
Use doubles.
2 × $8.50 is $17.
Double 2 is 4: 4 × $8.50 is $34.
The cost of 4 movie tickets is about $34.

> You can also estimate by rounding.
> Round $8.45 to the nearest dollar.
> $8.00 × 4 = $32.00.
> The cost of 4 movie tickets is about $32.00.

➤ Trudie paid $31.14 for 6 pairs of toe socks.
Estimate the cost of 1 pair.

Estimate: $31.14 ÷ 6

$31.14 is close to $30.
$30 ÷ 6 = $5.00
One pair of socks cost about $5.00.

Try These

1. Estimate each product.
   a) 2.35 × 7   **b)** 6.9 × 8   **c)** 29.9 × 6   **d)** 1.96 × 8

   _____   _____   _____   _____

2. Estimate each quotient.
   a) 9.6 ÷ 2   **b)** 16.8 ÷ 4   **c)** 2.98 ÷ 3   **d)** 155.1 ÷ 5

   _____   _____   _____   _____

1. Estimate each product or quotient.
   a) 39.8×4 **b)** 0.98×6 **c)** 8.79×5 **d)** 11.2×9

   _____   _____   _____   _____

   e) $29.4 \div 7$ **f)** $13.9 \div 2$ **g)** $49.86 \div 5$ **h)** $8.84 \div 3$

   _____   _____   _____   _____

2. **a)** Here is a list of some school supplies Cheryl needs.
   Estimate the cost of each kind of item.

Item	Price	Number Needed	Estimated Cost
Pencils	$0.77 each	5	
Highlighters	$2.39 each	2	
File Folders	$1.15 each	8	
Pens	$1.49 each	6	
Binders	$3.89 each	2	

   b) Estimate the total cost of all the supplies. _____

3. Five friends will share the cost of a $19.59 pizza.

   About how much will each person pay? _____

4. Nestoria worked 29.8 hours over 5 days last week.

   About how many hours did she work each day? _____

Stretch Your Thinking

Jackie's rabbit travelled 5.95 m in 3 jumps.
About how many centimetres long was each jump?

_____

_____

Multiplying Decimals with Tenths

Quick Review

Randolf jogged around the park 3 times.
The perimeter of the park is 2.9 km.
How far did Randolf jog?

➤ Multiply: 2.9×3

Use what you know about multiplying whole numbers.

$$\begin{array}{r} 2.9 \\ \times\ \ 3 \\ \hline 2.7 \\ +\ 6.0 \\ \hline 8.7 \end{array}$$

$2.7 \longleftarrow$ ────── 3×9 tenths = 27 tenths or 2.7

$+ 6.0 \longleftarrow$ ───── 3×2 ones = 6 ones, or 6.0

$8.7 \longleftarrow$ ──── $2.7 + 6.0 = 8.7$

➤ Estimate to check your answer.
Round 2.9 to 3.
$3 \times 3 = 9$
9 is close to 8.7, so the answer is reasonable.

Randolf jogged 8.7 km.

Try These

1. Find each product.

   a) 5.6
   $\underline{\times 2}$

   b) 7.8
   $\underline{\times 3}$

   c) 0.9
   $\underline{\times 4}$

   d) 12.3
   $\underline{\times 8}$

   e) 20.6
   $\underline{\times 8}$

2. Circle the number that is closest to the product.

   a) 7.2×8 50   54   56

   b) 10.9×9 99   101   104

1. Play this game with a partner.
   You will need 20 counters of one colour and 20 of another colour.

   Take turns:
   ➤ Choose one number from each factor box.
     Multiply to find the product.
   ➤ If the product is not covered on the game board, cover it with one of
     your counters.
   ➤ The first player to cover 4 products in a row (horizontally, vertically,
     or diagonally) is the winner.

41.5	11.7	7.8	20.4	30.6
49.8	10.2	24.9	33.5	49.2
61.5	26.8	25.5	33.2	16.6
15.3	13.4	40.2	19.5	23.4
15.6	36.9	73.8	20.1	24.6

Factor Boxes

2   5
  4
3   6

5.1   8.3
  6.7
3.9   12.3

Stretch Your Thinking

Without multiplying, tell what you know about the product of 11.6 and 7.

_____

_____

_____

Multiplying Decimals with Hundredths

At Home
At School

Quick Review

The zookeeper feeds the baby camel 1.75 kg of food each day.
How much food does the camel eat in a week?

Multiply: 1.75×7

➤ Record the numbers without the decimal point.
Multiply as you would with whole numbers.

➤ Estimate to place the decimal point in the product.
1.75 is about 2.
$2 \times 7 = 14$, so place the decimal point after 12.

$$
\begin{array}{r}
175 \\
\times\ 7 \\
\hline
35 \\
490 \\
700 \\
\hline
12.25
\end{array}
$$

The baby camel eats 12.25 kg of food in a week.

Try These

1. Multiply. Estimate to place the decimal point in the product.

a) $\begin{array}{r} 1.56 \\ \times\ 4 \\ \hline \end{array}$

b) $\begin{array}{r} 7.05 \\ \times\ 7 \\ \hline \end{array}$

c) $\begin{array}{r} 6.94 \\ \times\ 5 \\ \hline \end{array}$

d) $\begin{array}{r} 2.86 \\ \times\ 3 \\ \hline \end{array}$

e) $\begin{array}{r} \$5.63 \\ \times\ 8 \\ \hline \end{array}$

f) $\begin{array}{r} 4.18 \\ \times\ 2 \\ \hline \end{array}$

g) $\begin{array}{r} 0.95 \\ \times\ 9 \\ \hline \end{array}$

h) $\begin{array}{r} 1.08 \\ \times\ 6 \\ \hline \end{array}$

i) $\begin{array}{r} 2.74 \\ \times\ 3 \\ \hline \end{array}$

j) $\begin{array}{r} 0.75 \\ \times\ 7 \\ \hline \end{array}$

k) $\begin{array}{r} 3.59 \\ \times\ 6 \\ \hline \end{array}$

l) $\begin{array}{r} \$8.32 \\ \times\ 8 \\ \hline \end{array}$

1. Find each product.
   Then, use the letters next to the products to solve this riddle:

What do you call a boy who counts on his fingers?

$3.73 \times 4 =$ _____ (G)

$5.84 \times 7 =$ _____ (M)

$1.73 \times 6 =$ _____ (Z)

$0.94 \times 8 =$ _____ (P)

$9.04 \times 5 =$ _____ (A)

$10.12 \times 4 =$ _____ (R)

$8.19 \times 7 =$ _____ (T)

$4.09 \times 8 =$ _____ (D)

$8.25 \times 3 =$ _____ (L)

$6.49 \times 9 =$ _____ (U)

$7.77 \times 6 =$ _____ (I)

$2.68 \times 2 =$ _____ (O)

$7.31 \times 9 =$ _____ (E)

$0.48 \times 6 =$ _____ (C)

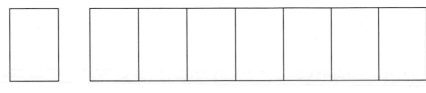

45.2   32.72 46.62 14.92 46.62 57.33 45.2 24.75

2.88   5.36   40.88   7.52   58.41   57.33   65.79   40.48

Stretch Your Thinking

Place these digits on the lines to make the greatest product.

2, 8, 6, 1, 5   _____ _____ • _____ _____ × _____

Dividing Decimals with Tenths

Quick Review

The race car driver drove around the track 4 times.
She travelled a total distance of 11.6 km.
How far is it around the track?

Divide: 11.6 ÷ 4

➤ Record the numbers without the decimal point.
  Divide as you would with whole numbers.
  $4\overline{)11^36}$
     2 9

➤ Estimate to place the decimal point.
  11.6 is close to 12.
  12 ÷ 4 = 3
  So, 11.6 ÷ 4 is a little less than 3.
  The answer must be 2.9.

➤ Check by multiplying: 2.9 × 4 = 11.6
  It is 2.9 km around the track.

Try These

1. Estimate each quotient.
   a) 37.4 ÷ 6   b) 2.9 ÷ 3   c) 74.8 ÷ 5

   _____   _____   _____

2. Divide.
   a) $8\overline{)16.8}$ b) $3\overline{)37.5}$ c) $6\overline{)38.4}$

   d) $4\overline{)13.6}$ e) $9\overline{)46.8}$ f) $2\overline{)1.4}$

1. Play this game with a partner.
   You will need:
   24 counters
   paper and pencils
   calculator

   Place a counter on each box of the game board.
   Take turns:
   ➤ Take a counter from the game board.
   ➤ Use paper and pencil to find the quotient.
   ➤ Have your opponent use a calculator to check.
   ➤ If your answer is right, keep the counter.
      If your answer is wrong, set the counter aside.
   ➤ Continue playing until all the counters are removed from the
      game board.
   ➤ The player with the most counters wins.

94.8 ÷ 3	59.1 ÷ 3	291.6 ÷ 3	75.6 ÷ 9	51.2 ÷ 4	20.7 ÷ 3
8.4 ÷ 6	22.8 ÷ 4	17.6 ÷ 2	170.4 ÷ 6	112.5 ÷ 3	58.8 ÷ 6
6.08 ÷ 8	73.8 ÷ 2	68.5 ÷ 5	33.3 ÷ 9	4.5 ÷ 9	34.5 ÷ 5
163.7 ÷ 7	78.4 ÷ 8	2.7 ÷ 3	84.6 ÷ 9	13.5 ÷ 3	289.8 ÷ 9

Stretch Your Thinking ·

If you divide a decimal by 4, the quotient is 4.3.

What would the quotient be if you divide the number by 2? _____

What is the number? _____

Dividing Decimals with Hundredths

At Home
At School

Quick Review

Six bottles of strawberry fruit punch contain 8.16 L of punch. What is the capacity of 1 bottle?

Divide: 8.16 ÷ 6

➤ Record the numbers without the decimal point.
Divide as you would with whole numbers.

$6 \overline{\smash{\big)}8^2 1^3 6}$
     1 3 6

➤ Estimate to place the decimal point.
8 ÷ 6 is a little more than 1.
The answer must be 1.36.

➤ Check by multiplying:
1.36 × 6 = 8.16
The capacity of 1 bottle is 1.36 L.

Try These

1. Estimate each quotient.
   a) 5.73 ÷ 2   b) 28.45 ÷ 7   c) 19.85 ÷ 4

   _____   _____   _____

2. Divide.
   a) 6⟌29.28   b) 5⟌9.45   c) 3⟌14.22

   d) 4⟌0.96   e) 2⟌73.84   f) 7⟌$24.43

1. Find the cost of one item. Show your work.

   a)

   b)

   c)

   _____

   _____

   _____

   d)

   e)

   f)

   _____

   _____

   _____

2. Terri-Ann cut a 6.24-m length of ribbon into 8 equal pieces. How long was each piece? Give your answer in as many different units as you can.

   _____

3. Juan's hot tub is in the shape of a regular hexagon. The perimeter of the hot tub is 10.92 m. What is the length of each side?

   _____

4. Can 5 people share $6.33 equally? Explain.

   _____

   _____

Stretch Your Thinking

Three friends are sharing equally the cost of a bag of oranges. How much do the oranges cost? Give as many answers as you can.

_____

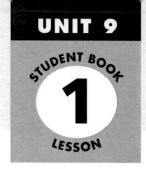
Measuring Linear Dimensions

Quick Review

At Home
At School

When you measure the length, width, height, thickness, or depth of an object, you are measuring a **linear dimension**.

Confederation Bridge is 12.9 km long.

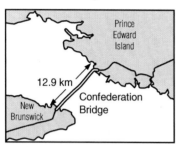

Prince Edward Island

12.9 km

New Brunswick

Confederation Bridge

This aquarium is 3.4 dm deep.

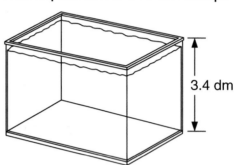

3.4 dm

A toonie is 1.8 mm thick.

1.8 mm

This billboard is 15 m wide and 6 m tall.

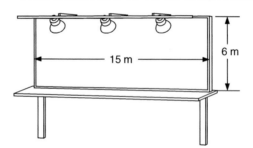

15 m

6 m

Try These

1. Which unit would you use to measure each item?

   a) the width of a ribbon _____ **b)** the distance from Brazil to Peru _____

   c) the thickness of a paper clip _____ **d)** the length of a truck _____

   e) the depth of a pond _____ **f)** the height of a telephone pole _____

2. Name:

   a) an object that is about 1 m tall _____

   b) a fruit that is about 15 cm long _____

   c) an animal that is about 1 dm long _____

1. Estimate. Then, measure each linear dimension.
   Complete the chart.

What to Measure	Unit	Estimate	Actual Measurement
the length of a crayon			
the height of a doorway			
the thickness of a penny			
the width of your hand			
the length of a paper clip			
the thickness of your thumb			

2. Name an object that is:

   a) taller than 5 m _____

   b) between 5 cm and 10 cm long _____

   c) about 30 mm long _____

   d) between 2 cm and 3 cm thick _____

Stretch Your Thinking

Find a box. Measure its dimensions. Record your results.

_____

_____

Relating Units of Measure

Quick Review

There are relationships among the units you use to measure length.

➤ You can read the length of this shoe in several ways.

The shoe is 17 cm long.

Since 1 cm is 10 mm, then 17 cm is 170 mm. The shoe is 170 mm long.

Since 1 cm is 0.1 dm, then 17 cm is 1.7 dm. The shoe is 1.7 dm long.

Since 1 cm is 0.01 m, then 17 cm is 0.17 m. The shoe is 0.17 m long.

1 mm = 0.1 cm	1 dm = 100 mm	1 m = 1000 mm
1 mm = 0.01 dm	1 dm = 10 cm	1 m = 100 cm
	1 dm = 0.1 m	1 m = 10 dm
1 cm = 10 mm		
1 cm = 0.1 dm		
1 cm = 0.01 m		1 km = 1000 m

Try These

1. Record each measure in millimetres, decimetres, and metres.

   a) 7 cm _____ **b)** 56 cm _____

   c) 13 cm _____ **d)** 40 cm _____

2. Record each measure in millimetres, centimetres, and decimetres.

   a) 4 m _____ **b)** 6 m _____

   c) 3.2 m _____ **d)** 40 m _____

3. Use =, <, or > to make each statement true.

   a) 4.16 m _____ 416 cm **b)** 75 cm _____ 7.9 dm **c)** 7.2 dm _____ 72 mm

1. Complete.

   a) 53 cm = _____ m   **b)** 4.1 dm = _____ cm   **c)** 85 mm = _____ cm

   d) 0.25 m = _____ cm   **e)** 8.6 dm = _____ mm   **f)** 25 cm = _____ mm

2. Write each length using 3 different units.

   a) 60 mm _____   **b)** 4 cm _____

   c) 0.03 m _____   **d)** 2.5 dm _____

3. Here are the lengths of 5 types of eggs.

Type of Egg	Length
Canada Goose	8.6 cm
Robin	1.9 cm
Hummingbird	13 mm
Ostrich	1.8 dm
Cuckoo	35 mm

   a) Which is longer, a robin egg

   or a cuckoo egg? _____

   b) Which is shorter, a hummingbird egg

   or a robin egg? _____

   c) About how many times as long as

   a Canada goose egg is an ostrich egg? _____

   d) Put the eggs in order from shortest to longest.

   _____

4. Barbeau Peak is 2.66 km tall. Mount Carleton is 817 m tall.

   Which mountain is taller? _____   How much taller is it? _____

5. Draw a line 9 cm long. Write its length using 3 other units.

   _____

Which would you rather have, a pile of loonies 350 mm tall or a pile of loonies 0.49 m tall? Explain.

_____

_____

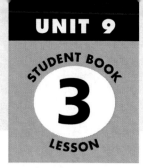
Using Non-Standard Units to Estimate Lengths

At Home
At School

Quick Review

➤ Metres and kilometres are **standard units**.
You use them to estimate and measure long lengths.

➤ Units such as baseball bats, car lengths, and strides are
non-standard units.
They can also be used to estimate and measure long lengths.

➤ A baseball bat is shorter than a car length.
The measure of a distance in baseball bats will be greater than the
measure of the same distance in car lengths.

Try These

1. About how many broomsticks long is the sidewalk?

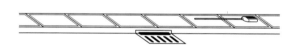

_____

2. About how many strides long is the dock?

_____

3. About how many car lengths tall is the building?

_____

4. About how many school bus lengths tall is the tree?

_____

1. Suppose you do not have a ruler, a metre stick, or a measuring tape. Explain how you would measure each of the following using a non-standard unit.
    a) the distance from your house to the bus stop

    _____

    b) the height of a telephone pole

    _____

    _____

    c) the length of a long piece of rope

    _____

    _____

2. Estimate each distance in strides.
   Then measure to check your estimates.
    a) from the front door to the street

    Estimate: _____   Measurement: _____
    b) from one end of the room to the other end

    Estimate: _____   Measurement: _____

3. Throw a beanbag or a rolled-up sock as far as you can.
   Choose a non-standard unit to measure the distance.
   Estimate first. Then measure the distance.

    Estimate: _____   Measurement: _____

Stretch Your Thinking

Describe a situation when it would not be appropriate to measure a long length using a non-standard unit.

_____

_____

_____

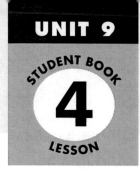
Measuring Distance Around a Circular Object

At Home
At School

Quick Review

The distance around a circular object is its **circumference**.
Here is one way to find the circumference of a circular object.
Use string and a ruler.

➤ Cut a length of string equal to the circumference of the object.

➤ Measure the string.

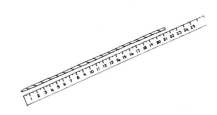

The circumference of the soup can is 21.5 cm.

Try These

1. Which unit would you use to measure the circumference of each object?

   a) a merry-go-round _____   **b)** a drinking glass _____

   c) a flower stem _____   **d)** a planet _____

2. Estimate first. Then find the circumference of each object.

   a) a jar lid _____   **b)** a button _____

   c) a wheel _____   **d)** a mug _____

3. Find an object with each circumference. Measure to check.

   a) between 10 cm and 20 cm _____

   b) about 30 cm _____

1. Name an object whose circumference you would measure using:

   a) millimetres _____

   b) centimetres _____

   c) metres _____

   d) kilometres _____

2. Match each object with an estimate of its circumference:
   175 cm, 3.2 cm, 7222 km, 40 054 km, 14 cm, 90 cm

   a) Earth _____

   b) a ballpoint pen _____

   c) a chicken egg _____

   d) a bicycle wheel _____

   e) a dinner plate _____

   f) Pluto _____

3. Estimate the circumference of each circle.
   Measure to check your estimate.
   Complete the chart.

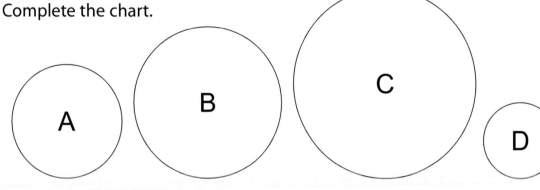

Circle	A	B	C	D
Estimate				
Measure				

Stretch Your Thinking

Draw a rectangle whose perimeter is
approximately the same length as the
circumference of this circle.

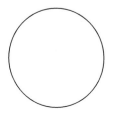

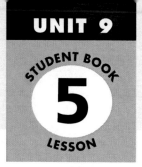
Using Grids to Find Perimeter and Area

At Home
At School

Quick Review

➤ One way to find the *perimeter* of this figure is to count the units along the outside of the figure.

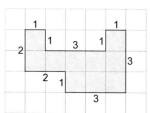

Each side of every square on this grid is 1 cm long.

The perimeter is 18 cm.

➤ One way to find the *area* of this figure is to count the squares inside the figure.

You can keep track of the counting by dividing the figure into rectangles and labelling each rectangle with the number of squares.

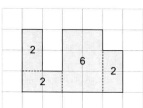

Each square on the grid has an area of 1 cm².

The area of the figure is 12 cm².

Try These

Find the perimeter and area of each figure.

1.
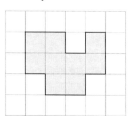

Perimeter: _____

Area: _____

2.
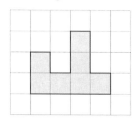

Perimeter: _____

Area: _____

3.
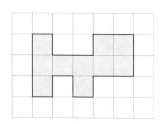

Perimeter: _____

Area: _____

1. Find the perimeter and area of each figure.
   Record your results in the chart.

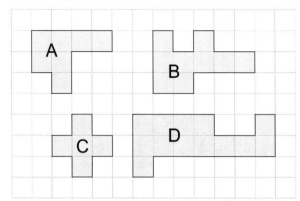

Figure	Perimeter	Area
A		
B		
C		
D		

2. Order the figures in question 1 from:

   a) least to greatest perimeter _____

   b) greatest to least area _____

3. Use the 1-cm grid below. Draw only on the lines.
   Draw 3 different figures with a perimeter of 10 cm.
   Record the area on each figure.

Change this figure so that it has a
lesser perimeter and a greater area.

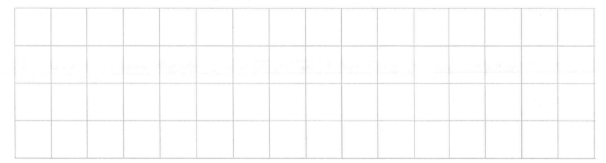

Measuring to Find Perimeter

Quick Review

➤ To find the perimeter of a polygon, measure the lengths of its sides, then add.
Perimeter = 3 cm + 2.5 cm + 5.4 cm + 2.6 cm
Perimeter = 13.5 cm

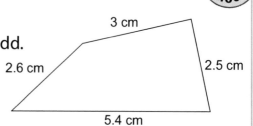

➤ Some polygons are too large to draw on a page.
A polygon like this is drawn to **scale**.
The drawing is similar to the polygon.
It has the same shape as the polygon, but it is smaller.
The length of each side is given.
To find the perimeter of the polygon, add the lengths of its sides.

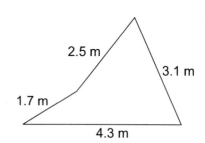

Perimeter = 3.1 m + 4.3 m + 1.7 m + 2.5 m
Perimeter = 11.6 m

Try These

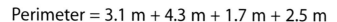

Find the perimeter of each figure.

1.

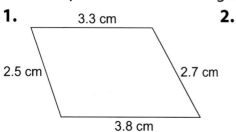

2.

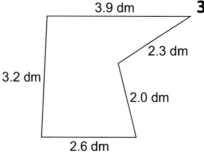

3.

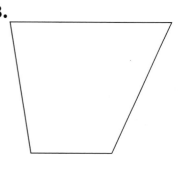

Perimeter = _____   Perimeter = _____   Perimeter = _____

1. For each object in the chart, choose a unit of measure.
   Estimate and then find the perimeter of each object.

Object	Unit	Estimate	Perimeter
a door			
a magazine			
a window			
a table top			
an envelope			
a floor tile			

2. Find the perimeter of each figure or region.

   a) a square garden with 6.2 m sides _____

   b) a triangle with sides 23 cm, 12.8 cm, and 18.9 cm _____

   c) a rectangular park with sides 0.9 km and 1.4 km _____

   d) a pentagon with sides 3.8 cm, 4.6 cm, 2.8 cm, 5 cm, and 3.1 cm _____

   e) an equilateral triangle with 7.8 mm sides _____

Stretch Your Thinking

The perimeter of a rectangle is 67.8 cm.
What might the dimensions of the rectangle be?

_____

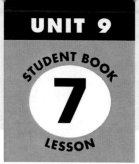
Calculating the Perimeter of a Rectangle

Quick Review

Here are two different rules for finding the perimeter of a rectangle.
Each rule can be expressed by a **formula**.

➤ Multiply the length by 2.
Multiply the width by 2.
Then add.

$2 \times 4 = 8$
$2 \times 3 = 6$
$8 + 6 = 14$
Perimeter = 14 units

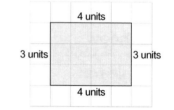

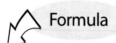
Formula

Perimeter = $2 \times$ length $+ 2 \times$ width

➤ Add the length and width.
Then multiply by 2.

$4 + 3 = 7$
$7 \times 2 = 14$
Perimeter = 14 units

Formula

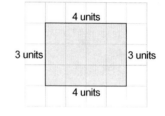

Perimeter = (length + width) $\times 2$

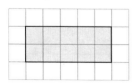
Try These

Find the perimeter of each rectangle in units.

1.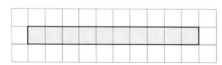

2.

3.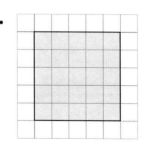

Perimeter = _____   Perimeter = _____   Perimeter = _____

1. Use a formula to find the perimeter of each rectangle. Show your work.

a)
18 m
12 m

b)
45 dm
45 dm

c)
10 km
4 km

_____

_____

_____

d)
6.5 m
1.5 m

e)
8.2 m
3.1 m

f)
4.7 km
1.1 km

_____

_____

_____

2. Measure the length and width of each object to the nearest unit.
    Use these dimensions to find the perimeter. Show your work.

a) your math book

Length: _____

Width: _____

b) a calculator

Length: _____

Width: _____

c) a window

Length: _____

Width: _____

_____

_____

_____

Stretch Your Thinking

Andy's rectangular garden is 3 times as long as it is wide. The perimeter of the garden is 56 m. What are the dimensions of Andy's garden?

_____

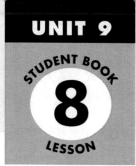

Calculating the Area of a Rectangle

Quick Review

Here is one way to find the area of a rectangle.

➤ Measure the length: 8 cm.

➤ Measure the width: 4 cm.

8 cm

4 cm

➤ Multiply the length by the width.
$8 \times 4 = 32$
So, the area of the rectangle is 32 cm².

Rule: ➡ To find the area of a rectangle, multiply the length by the width.

Formula: ➡ Area = length × width

Try These

Find the area of each rectangle.
Complete the chart.

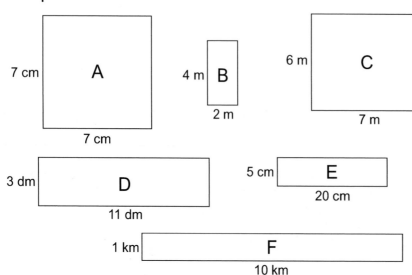

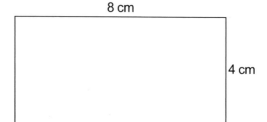

7 cm   A   7 cm

4 m B   2 m

6 m   C   7 m

3 dm D 11 dm

5 cm E 20 cm

1 km F 10 km

Figure	Area
A	
B	
C	
D	
E	
F	

Practice

1. Find the area of each rectangle.

   a) 5.5 km, 4.0 km

   b) 0.9 m, 4.0 m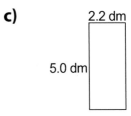

   c) 2.2 dm, 5.0 dm

   Area = _____   Area = _____   Area = _____

2. Measure the length and width of each object to the nearest unit.
   Use these dimensions to find the area. Record your work in the chart.

Object	Length	Width	Area
a tabletop			
the classroom floor			
a sheet of paper			
a page from a magazine			

3. Draw a rectangle with
   an area of 12 cm².
   Label the side lengths.

Stretch Your Thinking

Find the area of the shaded
part of the rectangle.
Show all your work.

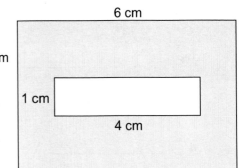

_____

_____

_____

_____

Finding the Area of an Irregular Polygon

Quick Review

Here is one way to find the
area of this irregular polygon.

➤ Divide the polygon
into sections.

➤ Find the area of
the rectangle.

➤ Draw broken lines to
make a rectangle for
the triangle.

Use the area of the rectangle to figure out the area of the triangle.

➤ Add the areas of the sections to find the area of the polygon.

$2 + 10 = 12$

The area of the polygon is 12 square units.

Try These

Find the area for each polygon in square units.

1.

Area = _____

2.

Area = _____

3.

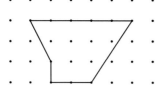

Area = _____

4.

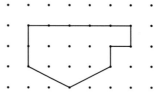

Area = _____

Practice

1. Find the area of each figure in square units. Record the areas in the chart.

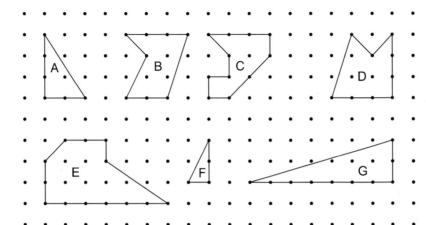

Figure	Area (square units)
A	
B	
C	
D	
E	
F	
G	

2. Order the figures in question 1 from least to greatest area.

_____

3. Draw 2 irregular polygons, each with an area of $12\frac{1}{2}$ square units.

Stretch Your Thinking

Divide the figure into 4 congruent parts. Show 3 different ways.

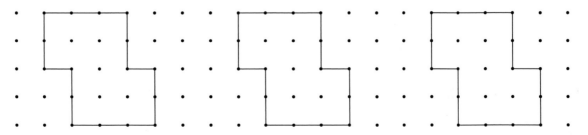

What is the area of each congruent part? _____

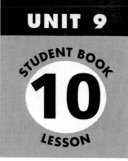
Estimating Area

At Home
At School

Quick Review

Here are 2 ways to estimate the area of this figure.

➤ Draw a large rectangle inside the figure.
Find the area of the rectangle: $9 \times 3 = 27$
Count the whole squares and part squares
outside the rectangle: about 20
Add to find the total: $27 + 20 = 47$
Area of the figure: about 47 square units

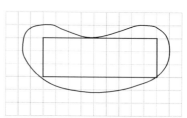

➤ Draw a rectangle around the figure.
Find the area of the rectangle: $12 \times 6 = 72$
Count the whole squares and part squares
outside the figure: about 24
Subtract this number from the area of
the rectangle: $72 - 24 = 48$
Area of the figure: about 48 square units

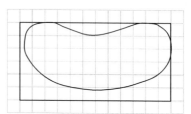

Try These

Find the approximate area of each figure in square units.

1.

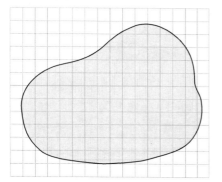

Area = _____

2.

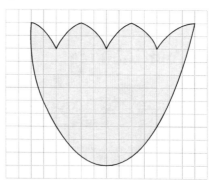

Area = _____

1. Trace a classroom object on the 1-cm grid below.
   Find the approximate area of your tracing.

2. Draw a rectangle that has about the same area as your object tracing.

Stretch Your Thinking

Explain how you could find the approximate area of a leaf.

_____

_____

Patterns in Multiplication

Quick Review

The order in which you multiply factors does not matter.
You can rearrange factors to make multiplication easier.

 Multiply: $4 \times 300 \times 15$

$4 \times 300 \times 15$ is the same as
$4 \times 15 \times 300$
Multiply: $4 \times 15 = 60$
Multiply: $60 \times 300 = 18\ 000$
So, $4 \times 300 \times 15 = 18\ 000$

Multiply: 15×39

15×39 is 15 less than 15×40
$15 \times 40 = 600$
$600 - 15 = 585$
So, $15 \times 39 = 585$

Here are 2 ways to find a missing factor.

➤ $\square \times 7 = 56$
You know that $8 \times 7 = 56$
So, the missing factor is 8.

➤ $325 = 25 \times \square$
Use a calculator.
Divide: $325 \div 25 = 13$
So, $325 = 25 \times 13$
The missing factor is 13.

Try These

1. Use mental math to multiply.

a) $5 \times 18 \times 2 = $ _____

b) $2 \times 35 \times 5 = $ _____

c) $50 \times 41 \times 2 = $ _____

d) $10 \times 17 \times 3 = $ _____

2. a) Use mental math to multiply: $12 \times 30 = $ _____
b) Use this product to find:

$12 \times 29 = $ _____ $12 \times 31 = $ _____

3. Multiply: $10 \times 15 = $ _____

Use this product to find the missing factors.

a) _____ $\times 15 = 165$ **b)** $15 \times $ _____ $= 135$

1. Multiply.

   a) $4 \times 200 \times 7 = $ _____

   b) $5 \times 65 \times 2 = $ _____

   c) $2 \times 125 \times 5 = $ _____

   d) $3 \times 150 \times 10 = $ _____

   e) $7 \times 50 \times 2 = $ _____

   f) $6 \times 30 \times 10 = $ _____

2. Find each missing factor.

   a) $12 \times $ _____ $= 132$

   b) $6 \times $ _____ $= 72$

   c) $135 = $ _____ $\times 15$

   d) $144 = 8 \times $ _____

   e) _____ $\times 19 = 133$

   f) $275 = $ _____ $\times 11$

3. A payroll clerk wrote 30 cheques, each for the same amount.
   The total amount of the cheques was $750.
   What was the value of each cheque?
   Write the answer as a missing factor multiplication problem.

   _____

   _____

4. Explain how you would use mental math to find
   a) the product of $4 \times 7 \times 25$

   _____

   b) the product of $5 \times 9 \times 2 \times 40$

   _____

Stretch Your Thinking

How many zeros are in the product of $4 \times 25 \times 200$?
Explain.

_____

_____

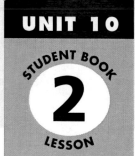
Exploring Patterns in Decimals with a Calculator

Quick Review

To change a fraction to a decimal, divide the numerator by the denominator.

To change $\frac{1}{4}$ to a decimal, press 1 $\boxed{\div}$ 4 $\boxed{=}$ to display $\boxed{0.25}$.

Look at these fractions and their decimal equivalents.

$\frac{1}{4} = 0.25$

$\frac{2}{4} = 0.5$

$\frac{3}{4} = 0.75$

$\frac{4}{4} = 1$

$\frac{5}{4} = 1.25$

$\frac{6}{4} = 1.5$

$\frac{7}{4} = 1.75$

$\frac{8}{4} = 2$

$\frac{9}{4} = 2.25$

$\frac{10}{4} = 2.5$

$\frac{11}{4} = 2.75$

The fractions grow by one-fourth each time.

The pattern rule for the numerators is:

Start at 1. Add 1 each time.

There are patterns in the decimals.

The pattern in the ones digits is:

0, 0, 0, 1, 1, 1, 1, 2, 2, 2, 2, . . .

The pattern rule for the decimals is:

Start at 0.25. Add 0.25 each time.

Try These

Use a calculator.

1. a) Change each fraction to a decimal.

$\frac{1}{8} =$ _____ $\frac{2}{8} =$ _____ $\frac{3}{8} =$ _____ $\frac{4}{8} =$ _____ $\frac{5}{8} =$ _____

   b) Write the next 5 fractions in the pattern.
   Change these fractions to decimals.

   _____

Use a calculator.

1. a) Change each fraction to a decimal.

$\frac{1}{10} =$ _____ $\frac{2}{10} =$ _____ $\frac{3}{10} =$ _____ $\frac{4}{10} =$ _____ $\frac{5}{10} =$ _____

b) Write the next 5 fractions in the pattern. Change fractions to decimals.

_____

c) Describe the pattern rule for the numerators of the fractions.

_____

d) Describe the pattern rule for the decimals.

_____

2. Complete each table.

a)

Fraction	Decimal
$\frac{1}{2}$	
$\frac{1}{3}$	
$\frac{1}{4}$	
$\frac{1}{5}$	
$\frac{1}{6}$	
$\frac{1}{7}$	
$\frac{1}{8}$	
$\frac{1}{9}$	
$\frac{1}{10}$	
$\frac{1}{11}$	

b)

Fraction	Decimal
$\frac{1}{6}$	
$\frac{2}{6}$	
$\frac{3}{6}$	
$\frac{4}{6}$	
$\frac{5}{6}$	
$\frac{6}{6}$	
$\frac{7}{6}$	
$\frac{8}{6}$	
$\frac{9}{6}$	
$\frac{10}{6}$	

3. Describe the patterns in the fractions in the tables in question 2.

a) _____

b) _____

Stretch Your Thinking

1. a) Change each fraction to a decimal: $\frac{1}{25} =$ _____ $\frac{2}{25} =$ _____ $\frac{3}{25} =$ _____

b) Predict the decimal for: $\frac{4}{25}$ _____ $\frac{5}{25}$ _____ $\frac{6}{25}$ _____

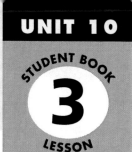

Graphing Patterns

Quick Review

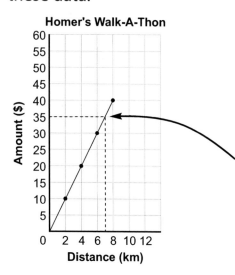

This table shows Homer's pledges for a charity walk-a-thon.

You can use a line graph to show these data.

Distance (km)	Amount ($)
2	10
4	20
6	30
8	40

Homer's Walk-A-Thon

From the graph, you can see that Homer will make $35 in pledges if he completes 7 km of the walk.

Try These

Use the table and line graph above.

1. Write the pattern rule for the amount of money.

_____

2. How much will Homer take in if he walks 3 km? _____ 5 km? _____

3. Predict how much Homer will take in if he walks 12 km.

Explain._____

1. a) Use toothpicks to build Frame 4 and Frame 5 of this growing pattern.
       Draw a picture of each frame.

Frame 1   Frame 2   Frame 3

   b) Record the data in the table.

Frame Number	Number of Toothpicks
1	
2	
3	
4	
5	

   c) Draw a line graph to show the data.

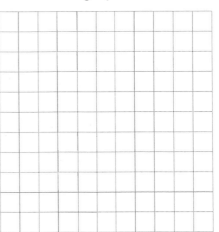

   d) Predict the number of toothpicks for Frame 15. _____
      Explain how you make your prediction.

      _____

      _____

      _____

Stretch Your Thinking

Look at the data in this table.
Write the pattern rules for
the input and output numbers.

_____

_____

Input	Output
150	300
162	324
174	348
186	372
198	396
210	420

Another Number Pattern

Quick Review

Look at this number pattern.

1, 1, 2, 3, 5, 8, 13, 21, . . .

This number pattern is called the **Fibonacci sequence**.

The first 2 terms of the Fibonacci sequence are 1 and 1.
After the first 2 terms, each term is the sum of the previous 2 terms.

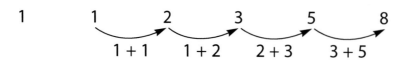

Any term in the Fibonacci sequence is called a **Fibonacci number**.
Fibonacci numbers are often found in nature.

Try These

1. Write the Fibonacci number suggested by each picture.

   a)

   _____

   b)

   _____

   c)

   _____

   d)

   _____

   e)

   _____

   f)

   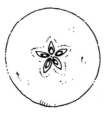

   _____

1. a) Write the first 16 numbers in the Fibonacci sequence.

_____

b) Choose any 4 consecutive terms. _____

Multiply the 2 middle terms. _____

Multiply the other 2 terms. _____

c) Repeat with 2 different groups of 4 consecutive terms.

_____

_____

d) What is the pattern? _____

_____

2. a) Dennis says that the sum of any 10 consecutive Fibonacci numbers is divisible by 11. Is he correct?

_____

_____

b) Repeat with a different set of 10 consecutive terms. What did you find out?

_____

_____

Stretch Your Thinking

A jar holds black, red, blue, and green marbles. 13 marbles are black. The red and blue marbles together total 13. There are more blue than red marbles. There are 13 less blue marbles than green marbles. The numbers of each colour of marbles are part of the Fibonacci sequence. How many marbles of each colour are there?

_____

_____

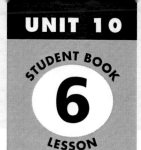
Quick Review

This is a tiling pattern.
It is made of irregular octagons.

The pattern uses these octagons:

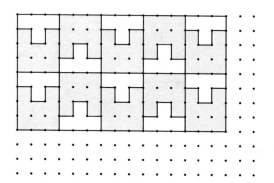

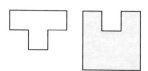

Arrange pairs of octagons to form rectangles.

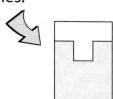

To continue the pattern, add rectangles to the pattern.

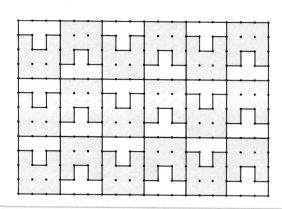

This rectangle is 3 units wide and 4 units long.

Try These

1. Here is a tiling pattern.
    a) What figures are used in the pattern?

    _____

    b) Extend the pattern one more row.
    c) How many of each figure would be in a pattern that is 15 units by 10 units?

    _____

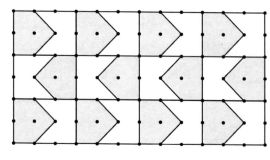

1. Here is the beginning of a tiling pattern.

    a) What figures do you see in the pattern?

    _____

    b) Extend the pattern 1 more row and
    1 more column.

    c) How many of each figure would be in a
    pattern that is 24 units by 24 units?

    _____

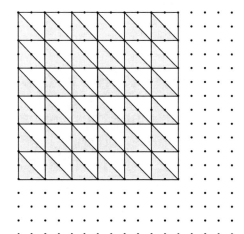

2. **a)** Use the grid below.
    Create a tiling pattern with 2 figures.

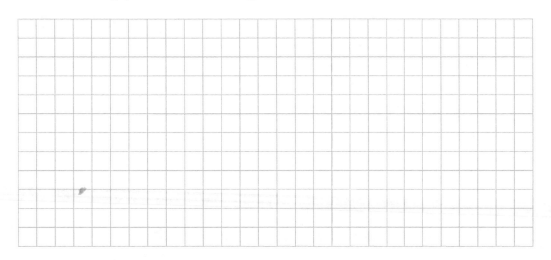

    b) Describe your pattern.

    _____

    _____

Stretch Your Thinking

How many of each of these figures would it take
to fill a space 24 units by 18 units? Explain.

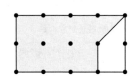

_____

_____

_____

The Likelihood of Events

Quick Review

At Home
At School

This spinner has 8 equal sectors.
Suppose you spin the pointer once.
What is the **likelihood** of each outcome?
- The pointer lands on an odd number.
- The pointer lands on an even number.
- The pointer lands on a number.
- The pointer lands on a 5.

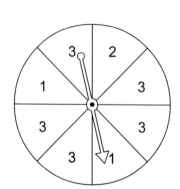

➤ 7 of the numbers are odd. It is **likely** that the pointer lands on an odd number.

➤ All of the sectors have a number. It is **certain** that the pointer lands on a number.

➤ Only 1 of the numbers is even. It is **unlikely** that the pointer lands on an even number.

➤ There are no 5s on the spinner. It is **impossible** for the pointer to land on a 5.

Try These

1. Describe each outcome. Use: likely, unlikely, certain, impossible.

   a) You will see your teacher next Saturday. _____

   b) The sun will set tonight. _____

   c) You will meet a talking frog. _____

   d) Flowers will grow in the spring. _____

2. Design a 4-part spinner with these outcomes:
   - Red and blue are equally likely.
   - Green is likely.
   - Yellow is unlikely.

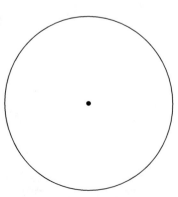

Practice

1. Suppose you spin this spinner once.
   Describe the likelihood of the pointer landing on:

   a) A _____   **b)** B _____

   c) a letter _____   **d)** Z _____

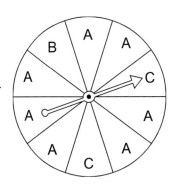

2. Draw 12 counters in the bag to show these outcomes:
   - Picking a red counter is likely.
   - Picking a purple counter is unlikely.
   - Picking a green counter is unlikely.
   - Picking a black counter is impossible.

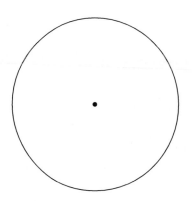

3. Design a spinner using 4 colours.
   Describe the likelihood of each outcome.

   _____

   _____

   _____

   _____

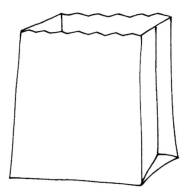

Stretch Your Thinking

Suppose you have pennies, nickels, and dimes. How many of each would you put in a bag to meet the following outcomes?
- Drawing a dime is likely.
- Drawing a nickel is unlikely.
- Drawing a penny is impossible.

_____

_____

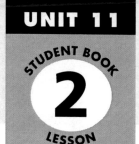

Calculating Probability

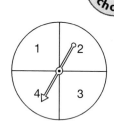

Quick Review

Here is a game for 2 players.
Players spin the pointers on both spinners,
then add the numbers that come up.
Player A gets a point if the sum is even.
Player B gets a point if the sum is odd.
Who will have more points after 20 turns?

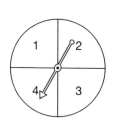

Organize the possible outcomes in a table.
From the table:

*   There are 16 possible outcomes.
*   8 outcomes are even sums.
*   8 outcomes are odd sums.

+	1	2	3	4
2	2	3	4	5
3	3	4	5	6
4	4	5	6	7
5	5	6	7	8

We say: "The probability of getting
an even sum is 8 out of 16."
"The probability of getting
an odd sum is 8 out of 16."

We write:

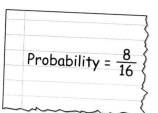

Probability = $\frac{8}{16}$

Try These

1. A coin is tossed.
    a) What are the possible outcomes? _____

    b) What is the probability of each outcome?

    _____

2. The pointers on these spinners are spun.
    The numbers that come up are multiplied.
    a) What are the possible outcomes?

    _____

    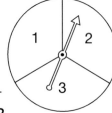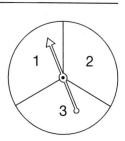

    b) What is the probability of each outcome?

    _____

    _____

1. Suppose you spin the pointers on these 2 spinners.
   One possible outcome is AA.
   List the other possible outcomes.

   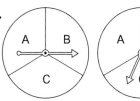

   _____

2. Suppose you and a friend are playing this game.
   You draw a card from a bag. Each card has one letter on it.
   There is one card for every letter in the words WHO WILL WIN.
   If you draw a W, you win.
   If your friend draws an L, she wins.
   Is this a fair game? Explain.

   _____

   _____

   _____

3. Maybelle and Kerry play a board game. They use a number cube labelled
   2, 4, 6, 8, 10, and 12. If Maybelle rolls a 1-digit number, she moves 1 space
   on the game board. If Kerry rolls a 2-digit number, he moves 1 space.
   Is this a fair game? Explain.

   _____

   _____

   _____

Stretch Your Thinking

Design a fair game that uses these 2 spinners.
Describe the rules of the game.

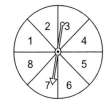

_____

_____

_____

_____

Probability and Fractions

Quick Review

Suppose you want to put gum balls in a toy machine to meet these outcomes:

- It is equally likely that a red, blue, or pink gum ball comes out.
- The probability of getting a green gum ball is $\frac{3}{6}$.

How many gum balls should you put in the machine?

The probability of getting green is $\frac{3}{6}$. So, 3 of every 6 gum balls must be green.

The total number of gum balls must be a multiple of 6.

There are many ways to fill the machine.

➤ You could use 6 gum balls: 3 green, 1 red, 1 blue, 1 pink.

➤ You could use 12 gum balls: 6 green, 2 red, 2 blue, 2 pink.

➤ You could use 18 gum balls: 9 green, 3 red, 3 blue, 3 pink.

Try These

1. Draw marbles in the bag to show these outcomes:
   - It is equally likely a blue or yellow marble will be pulled.
   - The probability of pulling a black marble is $\frac{2}{4}$.

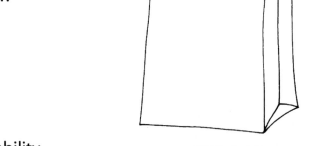

2. Write a fraction to show each probability.

   a) drawing a consonant _____

   b) drawing a vowel _____

3. Suppose you roll a 12-sided solid labelled 1 to 12.
   What fraction shows the probability of rolling a one-digit number? _____

160

1. Here are the results of rolling a
number cube several times.

Odd	Even
HHт HHт I	HHт HHт IIII

   a) How many times was the number cube rolled? _____

   b) What fraction of the rolls were odd numbers? _____

   c) What fraction of the rolls were even numbers? _____

2. Mason tossed a paper cup over and over.
The table shows the outcomes of his tosses.

Side	Bottom	Rim
HHт HHт III	III	IIII

   a) How many times did Mason toss the paper cup? _____

   b) What fraction of the tosses landed the cup on its side? _____

   On its bottom? _____ On its rim? _____

   c) What results would you expect in 100 tosses? _____

   _____

3. Suppose you spin this spinner 100 times.
About how many times will it land on A? _____

On B? _____

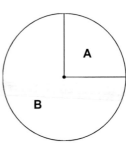

4. Draw a spinner that you think
will give 80 orange and
20 blue in 100 spins.

Design a spinner using at least 4 colours.
Suppose you spin the spinner 100 times.
Describe the probability of landing on each colour.

_____

_____

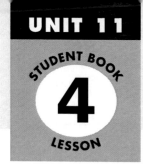
Tree Diagrams

At Home At School

Quick Review

Prepackaged lunches in the school cafeteria contain:
- a ham or a peanut-butter sandwich
- an apple or an orange
- juice or milk

How many different combinations of sandwich, fruit, and drink are there?
Draw a tree diagram.

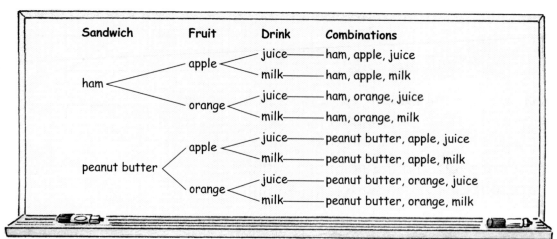

Sandwich	Fruit	Drink	Combinations

ham
- apple
  - juice — ham, apple, juice
  - milk — ham, apple, milk
- orange
  - juice — ham, orange, juice
  - milk — ham, orange, milk

peanut butter
- apple
  - juice — peanut butter, apple, juice
  - milk — peanut butter, apple, milk
- orange
  - juice — peanut butter, orange, juice
  - milk — peanut butter, orange, milk

There are 8 different combinations.

Try These

1. Use the tree diagram above.
   Suppose a student picks up a lunch package at random.
   Find the probability of the student having each of the following:

   a) a ham sandwich _____

   b) an apple _____

   c) a peanut-butter sandwich and milk _____

   d) a ham sandwich and an orange _____

   e) a ham sandwich, juice, and an apple _____

   f) a bologna sandwich _____

1. Suppose you flip a penny, a nickel, and a dime.
   Draw a tree diagram to show all the possible outcomes.
   Use H for heads and T for tails.

2. Use the tree diagram from question 1 to determine the probability of flipping each of these combinations:

   a) 2 heads and a tail _____

   b) 2 tails and a head _____

   c) 3 heads _____

   d) 1 tail _____

3. The ice-cream shop offers 3 different flavours of ice cream (vanilla, strawberry, cherry), 2 sauces (chocolate, marshmallow), and 2 toppings (nuts, sprinkles). Draw a tree diagram to show all the possible sundae orders with 1 flavour of ice cream, 1 sauce, and 1 topping.

Stretch Your Thinking

In question 1 above, what is the difference between the outcome, HHT and the outcome, HTH?

_____

_____

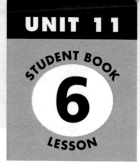
Probability in Games

Quick Review

Aaron and Lizzy play this game.
There are 26 cards in a bag.
Each card has a different letter of the alphabet on it.
Players take turns to draw a card.
If the letter on the card comes before M, Aaron gets a point.
Otherwise, Lizzy gets a point.
The cards are returned to the bag after each draw.
The player with the most points after 10 draws wins.

Is this a fair game?

There are 26 possible outcomes.
If Aaron draws a card with the letter A, B, C, D, E, F, G, H, I, J, K, or L
on it, he gets a point.
There are 12 ways for Aaron to get a point.
The probability of Aaron getting a point is $\frac{12}{26}$.
The probability of Lizzy getting a point is $\frac{14}{26}$.
So, this is not a fair game.

Try These

Think about the game Aaron and Lizzy played.

1. What is the probability of Aaron *not* getting a point? _____

2. What is the probability of Lizzy *not* getting a point? _____
3. How could you change the game to make it fair?

_____

_____

_____

_____

1. **a)** Play this game with a partner.
   You will need 2 number cubes, each labelled 1 to 6.
   ➤ Take turns to roll the number cubes.
   Player A gets a point if the number on each cube is the same.
   Player B gets a point if the numbers are different.
   ➤ The first player to get 10 points is the winner.
   ➤ Play the game 5 times.

   b) Is this a fair game? How do you know?

   _____

   _____

2. **a)** Design an unfair game that involves drawing numbers from a bag.
   Describe the rules of your game. Explain how you know the game is
   not fair.

   _____

   _____

   _____

   _____

   _____

   _____

   b) How could you change your game so that it is fair?

   _____

   _____

Stretch Your Thinking

In a game, there are 2 ways for Player A to win. The probability of Player A
winning is $\frac{1}{4}$.
How many different outcomes must the game have? _____

I Wonder...

Do people with the biggest hands also have the biggest feet?

Conduct your own survey to find out!

➤ Make some copies of the 1-cm grid on page 5 (or use graph paper).

➤ Find some willing participants.

➤ Trace each person's hand and foot on the grid (you may have to join sheets together)

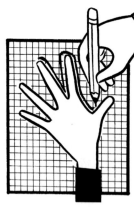

What is the area of each hand and each foot? How will you count up the part-squares?

Displaying your information in 2 separate bar graphs will give you an **instant picture** of the answer!

Show your graphs to someone and tell them what you've found out!

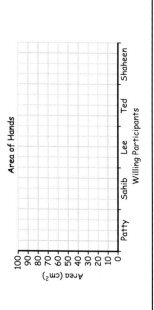

Mix Them Up!

You'll need:

▶ copies of the rhombus shown below (15 for each player)

▶ a number cube

The object of this game is to be the first to clear away all of your pieces.

Trace and cut out copies of this rhombus.

To begin, each player joins rhombuses to build 5 hexagons.

I have 10 thirds left. That's 3 and $\frac{1}{3}$!

On your turn:

▶ Roll the number cube. This will tell you **how many rhombuses** you may discard.

▶ Tell how much is left. You must say it 2 ways.

Special Rules

1. If you roll a 6, miss your turn.
2. If you roll a 3, give the other player 3 rhombuses to add to his or her collection.
3. If you forget to say how much is left, take 2 rhombuses from the other player.

First to clean up wins!

6

Bring It To Zero!

You'll need:

▶ 2 or more players

▶ a calculator

The object of this game is to bring each of the digits to 0 in the fewest number of moves.

Enter any 6-digit number into your calculator. You must have at least 3 decimal places and each digit must be different.

In turn, players choose any digit within that number and subtract whatever number they think will bring that digit to 0.

Once you have entered ▢, your turn is done and the calculator is passed to the next player. That player may then either choose a different digit, or work on the same one. The player to get the last 0 wins that round!

Now try it the other way!

Enter a 6-digit number below 500 and take turns **adding** to each digit. The first player to get to **1000** wins!

Think About It!

Is there enough in a small container of dental floss to go all the way around your room? More than once?

How can you tell without unrolling it?

3

Rocky Rectangles!

▶ Get 4 straws, all the same length.

▶ Arrange them into a square.

▶ Use a needle and thread to join the 4 corners, but not too tightly.

Place your square on the
1-cm grid on page 5.
What area have you fenced in?

You want to design a pen for
your dog.
Move corners in or out to see what happens to the area.

Which would make a better dog pen: a shape with
2 acute and 2 obtuse angles, or one with 4 right angles?

Smart Alec

Alec only had a 3-L pitcher and a 5-L pitcher.
Yet he managed to measure out exactly 1 L of cider.
How did that smart Alec do it?

Flipped!

If you flip a coin, how many possible ways can it land?

It either has to land 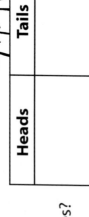 or 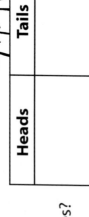 .

In other words, it will land **1 out of 2** possible ways.

Another way to say that is $\frac{1}{2}$.

So... does that mean you would
land on heads half the time?

Try it 10 times.
Record what you get each time.

Heads	Tails

What do you think
the results would be
if you tried it 20 times?
100 times?

How close to one half do you get?

TOO FUNNY Ha Ha Ha Ha

Why did the triangle
always go to the
square for advice?

*Because he always had
the right angle on things!*

Do you know what
I find odd in math?

Numbers not divisible by 2!

What did one decimal
say to the other?

Get the point?

Super Squares

Draw a nice neat square and mark 3 midpoints.

Connect the points as shown and cut along those lines.

You'll be left with a pentagon and 2 triangles.

How many different shapes can you make with these 3 pieces? Can you make one that looks like an animal?

Mirror, Mirror...

Where could you place a straight-sided mirror so that you could see:

2 circles?

4 circles?

6 circles?

more circles?

Fold

Math at Home

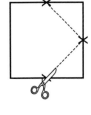

Distractions in 3-D

There's nowhere I can look around
And not see three-dimensional!
I see a prism in a tissue box
An accident? Or intentional?

My hamper is rectangular,
The TV is a cube.
Wait! Do I see a cylinder
In that left-over paper tube?

My closet is a virtual kingdom in 3-D
That hockey puck, my soccer ball,
A hat from Lee's party!

My bedposts are all pyramids
Of the hexagonal family.
I can't escape this madness!
These distractions in 3-D!

Math at Home 3

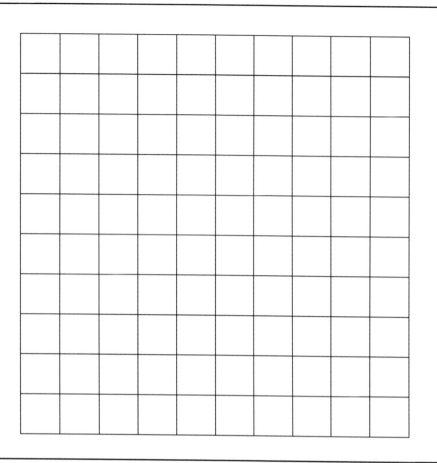

47 hundredths left to go!

Trace this grid to make additional copies.

Bonus!

If you can also say how much of your grid is left to colour, give yourself a bonus of 5 more hundredths.

Roll to a Whole!

You'll need:
▲ 2 number cubes
▲ 2 copies of the grid on page 5
▲ crayons or markers

The goal is to be the first to colour in one whole grid.

On your turn:

▲ Roll one number cube. This will tell you how many tenths you may colour in on your grid.

▲ Roll the second number cube. This will tell you how many hundredths you may colour in on your grid.

▲ Colour them in and say how much of your whole grid is coloured.

▲ Record that decimal number on a piece of paper and… that's the end of your turn!

Does it sound too easy?
Here are a couple rules you must obey:

1. If you forget to say your decimal number aloud, your partner gets an extra turn.

2. If you roll doubles, you must colour in that amount on the other player's grid.

Colour your grid in first to be the decimal champ!

Varying Volumes

The next time you have an empty paper towel tube, try this experiment!

▼ Cover one end of the tube with tape.
▼ Fill the tube with rice or beans.
▼ Pour the contents into a measuring cup.

▼ Cut the tube along its length and lay it flat.
It should look like a rectangle.
Mark the top and bottom edges.
▼ Now roll it back up from bottom to top and tape it up.
Don't forget to seal one end with tape.

Can you pour all of the contents of the measuring cup into your new container?
Is there room to spare?

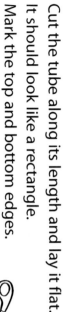

What can you say about the volume as the shape changes?

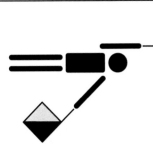

Who Knew?

Semaphore is an alphabet signalling system based on holding flags, with the arms at different angles, to represent letters or numbers.

Look up the code on the web.
What words can you make with only acute angles?

What's My Story?

This is a graph about something Rosie the Stone Mason did.
Can you guess what it is?

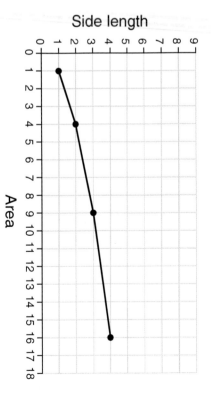

Side length

Area

Tell your own story with a line graph and ask someone to guess what it's about!

What's a forum?
A 2-um + a 2-um

What did the boy say when his mom asked him if his math test was hard?
No, but the answers were

What do you call matching Ls?
Parallels

Coordinated Shapes

Ethan drew some shapes on a coordinate grid.
The paths his pencil followed were like this:

Shape 1: B1, D4, D1, B1
Shape 2: C5, D7, G7, H5, C5
Shape 3: E3, G5, I3, G1, E3

Make your own Coordinated Shapes puzzle
for someone else to solve!

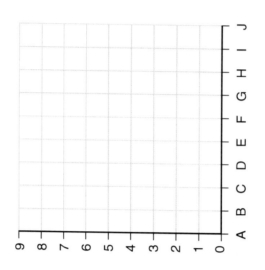

Tricky Toothpicks...

Arrange 12 toothpicks
to make a pattern like this:

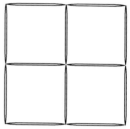

Move just 2 of them
to leave 7 squares!

Mathematics Acrobatics

Try this number trick out on a friend!

Ask her to...

▲ choose a number
▲ add 3
▲ multiply by 2
▲ add 4
▲ divide by 2
▲ subtract the original number

Now tell your friend that the number in her head is **5**!

Aren't you amazing! Does it work with any number?
What about decimal numbers?

You can make up your own number tricks if you
understand how they work... "Mind pictures" can help!

✔ 25

✔ + 3 ○○○

✔ × 2

✔ + 4 ○○○○

✔ ÷ 2 ○○○○○

✔ subtract the ○○○○○
original number

Now make up some of your own!

The next 4 pages fold in half to make an 8-page booklet.

Did You Know?

The most popular fruit in Canada is… apples!

That's right.

Canadians eat an *average* of 10 apples per month.

Are you about average?

Survey your family for a month and make a bar graph.

Do you have an average apple-eater in your family?

Above average?

Is there someone who needs to be reminded?

Keep That Still!

Carson the Culvert Cleaner has been called to clean out this culvert.

Will he enter it from left to right or right to left?

Optical illusions are about what your brain **thinks** it sees than what it actually sees.

In other words, all you have to do to see it both ways is just "change your mind"!

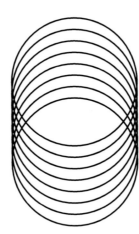

Fold

Math at Home

How many places?

What comes next?

Is this right?

Where do I put it?

Where do I start?

How do I know?

Kids Rule!

Rules! Rules! Rules! How do I keep them straight?

Was it this or was it that? Do it now? Or should I wait?

First I'm sure and then I'm not; my brain can sure get muddled.

Which rule is right for the job at hand?

Sometimes I feel befuddled!

But, ah… that's how it *used* to be, before I was this wise.

Then I worked with blocks and rods, 'til right before my eyes

My OWN rules began appearing through my new math lens.

Remembering is never a problem now…

'Cause now my Math Makes Sense!

1	2	3	4	5	6	7	8	9	10
11	12	13	14	15	16	17	18	19	20
21	22	23	24	25	26	27	28	29	30
31	32	33	34	35	36	37	38	39	40
41	42	43	44	45	46	47	48	49	50
51	52	53	54	55	56	57	58	59	60
61	62	63	64	65	66	67	68	69	70
71	72	73	74	75	76	77	78	79	80
81	82	83	84	85	86	87	88	89	90
91	92	93	94	95	96	97	98	99	100

Tricky Triangles

How many triangles can you make by joining any 3 dots?

Hint: *there are more than 20*

In the Bag

You'll need:

▶ a 100-chart (page 5)

▶ 12 small paper squares numbered 1 to 12

▶ 20 buttons (10 of one colour and 10 of another)

▶ a paper bag

The object of this game is to get rid of your buttons first!

▶ Place all number squares in the paper bag.

▶ In turn, take three squares from the bag…
No peeking!

▶ Multiply any two or three of the numbers together.

2	8	5

2 × 5   or   2 × 8   or   5 × 2 × 8

▶ With one of your buttons, cover the number on the 100-chart that represents the product you made.

▶ Now it's the next player's turn.

No two buttons can share the same square.
If you can't play, you'll have to wait for your next turn.

Clean up all of your buttons first and you are the champ!

Odd One Out

◯◯◯◯◯◯◯◯◯◯◯◯●

Once you figure out the strategy to guarantee a win, you'll be able to stump just about anyone!

Find a partner, then set out 13 counters (buttons, coins, etc.) in a line. 12 of them must be the same and 1 different.

In turn, starting with the first counter, you may take 1 or 2 counters (the choice is yours).

The idea is to not get into a position where you are forced to take the different coloured counter!

Hint: *Work backwards... think about what you DON'T want for a number.*

Ready for another challenge? Try it with 21 counters, where you can take 1, 2, or 3 counters on a turn!

Faster Than a Speeding Pencil!

Would you believe that you can multiply all of the numbers on your phone pad together in your head faster than I can do it on a calculator? It's true! But how can that be?

Challenge someone to a duel and try it out! Use what you know about zero.

How Many Are There Really?

×	0	1	2	3	4	5	6	7	8	9	10
0	0	0	0	0	0	0	0	0	0	0	0
1	0	1	2	3	4	5	6	7	8	9	10
2	0	2	4	6	8	10	12	14	16	18	20
3	0	3	6	9	12	15	18	21	24	27	30
4	0	4	8	12	16	20	24	28	32	36	40
5	0	5	10	15	20	25	30	35	40	45	50
6	0	6	12	18	24	30	36	42	48	54	60
7	0	7	14	21	28	35	42	49	56	63	70
8	0	8	16	24	32	40	48	56	64	72	80
9	0	9	18	27	36	45	54	63	72	81	90
10	0	10	20	30	40	50	60	70	80	90	100

Use what you already know!

Do you really need to memorize...

▼ Any number × 0? Probably not... cross them off.
▼ Any number × 1? Probably not... cross them off.
▼ Any number × 2? That's just like adding doubles.
▼ Any "turn around" fact (3 × 4 is the "turn around" of 4 × 3)? That gets rid of about half right there!

How many now? Are you surprised?

Who Knew?

How many toothpicks would you need to make 8 triangles? Make a prediction, then build your triangles to test it. Could it be made with fewer? Even fewer? Fewer still?

What do you call people in favour of tractors?

Pro-tractors

Who invented fractions?

Henry the Eighth

Who helped him?

Louis the Sixteenth

Would You Rather?

Imagine that you just got a new job for 1 month. Your employer gave you a choice of how you would be paid.

1. $5000 for the month
2. 1¢ the first day, then your pay would double each day until the month was up.

You gave it a quick think and, of course, jumped at the first choice… $5000 for just one month is a lot of money!

Did you make a good choice? Check it out!

On the Road Again!

You are heading out on another trip!

Is there a pattern to where distance signs are placed along the highway?

Find out by calculating the difference in distance between one sign and the next.

If there is a pattern, it should show up in the next few signs. Does the location make a difference?

Newport 15 km
Chelsea 13 km

Riddle Me

Homework doesn't always mean sitting at the table with a paper and pencil.

Practise your number sense in the kitchen while supper is cooking, out driving in the car, at the store shopping for groceries, or anywhere at all!

I'm thinking of a number …

It has 350 tens and 5 ones. Can you guess what it is?

Nifty Nines

Catch the pattern! What do you notice about the tens place in the answer?

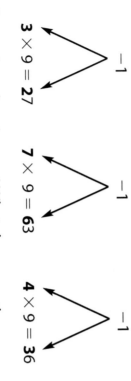

−1

$3 \times 9 = 27$ $7 \times 9 = 63$ $4 \times 9 = 36$

−1   −1

But wait… there's more! What do you notice when you add the digits in each answer?

Put these together and you'll never be stumped by 9 × *anything!*

The next 4 pages fold in half to make an 8-page booklet.

Fold

Math at Home

Numbers in columns, numbers in rows;
Start with a few and watch them grow.
Some say they're tough, but I can't be fooled!
'Cause I hunt for **patterns**… that's *my* secret tool!

I ask myself good questions on my noble pattern quest,
Self, I say, look carefully… What's the **diff**?
Where's the rest? Does it grow?
No, wait, it shrinks by 5. Eureka! This is it!
I can solve the puzzle when I find the one that fits!